TRANSPUTER
INSTRUCTION SET

a compiler writer's guide

Other titles in this series

Transputer Reference Manual
Transputer Development System
Communicating Process Architecture
Transputer Technical Notes
Transputer Instruction Set: a compiler writer's guide
Digital Signal Processing

TRANSPUTER INSTRUCTION SET

a compiler writer's guide

INMOS Limited

Prentice Hall
New York   London   Toronto   Sydney   Tokyo

First published 1988 by
Prentice Hall International (UK) Ltd,
66 Wood Lane End, Hemel Hempstead,
Hertfordshire, HP2 4RG
A division of
Simon & Schuster International Group

INMOS document number: 72 TRN 119 05

Printed and bound in Great Britain
at the University Press, Cambridge

CIP data are available

1 2 3 4 5   92 91 90 89 88

ISBN 0-13-929100-8

Contents

Preface

This book is the guide to the instruction set of the transputer family. A transputer is a single VLSI device with processor, memory and communication links for direct connection to other transputers. Transputers are designed to allow parallel systems to be built from collections of processors operating concurrently and communicating through links.

Although this book is the transputer instruction set definition and is intended to be a reference manual for programmers it is not set out in the 'traditional' form. This has been done quite deliberately. A traditional instruction set document contains brief descriptions of the individual instructions one by one — probably in alphabetic order of mnemonics — along with tables detailing the addressing modes available and the effects of the instruction on various flags, memory, registers etc. The more traditional form of document provides all the information about the instruction set — but leaves the reader to find out how best to use it. This was (perhaps) appropriate when the bulk of programming was being performed in assembly language. However when writing this book the following assumptions have been made

1. Assembly language programming lacks security.

2. Concurrent assembly language programming is even harder than traditional assembly language programming.

3. A language like occam provides a means for writing efficient concurrent programs for transputers as well as permitting formal verification through proof techniques.

4. Current compiler techniques, along with a well designed language and instruction set can provide high level language performance comparable to assembly language. In fact compiled code can often have higher performance as a compiler can automatically perform optimisations such as the use of constant tables, case selection jump tables and re-ordering of expression evaluation — techniques for all of these are included.

For these reasons this book introduces the transputer instruction set in terms of compiler writing. The intention is that programs for transputers are compiled from high level languages — such as occam, C, Fortran, Modula-2 etc. — into transputer code rather than being written at the assembly language level. Instructions are introduced to explain the compilation of various aspects of a high level language. The compilation of constructs of a high level language is given in terms of translations from occam code to sequences of transputer instructions. Algorithms suitable for implementation in a compiler are given for various constructs where careful choice of the compiled code can increase performance.

The high level programming language examples used in this book are in occam 2. Further details of this language can be found in the *occam 2 Reference Manual*. Compilation strategies for other languages can be developed by looking at the compilation of similar constructs in occam.

1 Introduction

This guide explains how high level programming language constructs can be translated into sequences of transputer instructions. It is assumed that a compiler for a language other than occam will translate a program into an occam like process, communicating with other processes only via occam channels. In this way, it is possible to freely mix languages in a system. In particular, occam can be used as a system description and configuration language, with other languages being used to write individual processes within the system.

The guide deals with various high level language constructs individually. Transputer instructions are introduced as they are needed in the implementation of these constructs. The instructions are normally explained when they are first introduced but in some cases this is delayed until a later section which is more appropriate.

Undefined values

In the definition of many instructions the values left in certain registers are said to be undefined. This should be taken as meaning that those values are not defined by INMOS and that INMOS does not claim that future transputers will behave in the same way as current transputers. No application should ever attempt to make use of the value that the current transputer implementations happen to provide in such cases.

Program notation

The language occam is used in this book both as a 'source language' to represent program constructs and program fragments to be compiled, and as a 'meta-language' to represent algorithms to produce compiled code and other examples. These two uses of occam will be distinguished by the use of an italic font for meta-language occam as in

$x := a + b$

and a teletype font for source language occam as in

```
x := a + b
```

Inside source language occam an italic font is used for 'meta-variables'. For example

```
PAR
  P
  Q
```

represents any two processes P and Q in a parallel construct.

The source language occam is the occam 2 language as defined in the *occam 2 Reference Manual*. The meta-language occam is based on occam 2 with some restrictions removed and extensions added to enable certain algorithms to be expressed more simply.

2 Basic concepts

2.1 The transputer instruction set

The instruction set is designed for simple and efficient compilation. All instructions have the same format, which is chosen to give a compact representation of the operations most frequently occurring in programs. Instructions are independent of the processor word-length, which may be any number of bytes. (The same instruction set could be used for a 16, 24 or 32 bit processor).

Enhanced versions of transputers provide added features — such as full hardware support of floating point arithmetic — so certain sections of this guide will be specific to transputers with those enhancements. This will be noted where appropriate.

2.2 Occam processes

A process starts, performs a number of actions, and then either stops or terminates successfully. Each action is either an assignment, an input or an output. An assignment sets the value of a variable, an input receives a value from a channel, and an output sends a value to a channel. The variable set by an assignment should not be accessible to any other process — the only method of transferring information from one process to another should be by using a channel.

At any time between it starting and terminating successfully a process may be ready to communicate on one or more of its channels. Each channel provides one way communication between two processes.

Communication is synchronised. If a channel is used for input in one process and output in another then communication takes place when both processes are ready. The inputting and outputting processes then proceed with the value output being copied from the outputting process to the inputting process.

Externally a process may be seen as being a 'black box' that, after starting, may or may not wish to communicate along one or more of its channels until it terminates successfully. A correctly functioning process will normally communicate data with the processes connected to it to perform the task it is designed to achieve, and then terminate successfully. However, a process can fail to communicate indefinitely. This failure of communication can be due to internal deadlock (where all internal processes are waiting to communicate with each other), internal livelock (where internal processes are only communicating with themselves and will never communicate with the outside world) or due to the process ceasing to execute without terminating successfully (in occam this is the **STOP** process).

The internal state of a process is not visible to the outside world and all interactions with the process occur via channel communication. This process model removes the problems associated with variable sharing. Also if a process is re-implemented to have the same behaviour and channel interface it can be immediately substituted in a system allowing for prototypes to be refined in stages into more efficient implementations.

2.3 Process scheduling

Each transputer executes an occam process. This process may itself consist of a number of concurrent processes. Concurrent processing within a transputer is implemented by sharing the processor time between the concurrent processes.

The processor executes one process at a time. The process being executed is called the current process, and the set of processes which are ready for execution is called the active set.

The processor can execute a process at one of two priority levels — level 0 for urgent processes and level 1 for less urgent processes. The processor will execute a level 0 process in preference to a level 1 process if both are active, so that the level 1 process will be interrupted.

The current process is executed until it is unable to proceed because it is waiting to input or output, waiting for the timer or it has been interrupted by a higher priority process. In addition time is shared between level 1 processes by timeslicing so that a level 1 process will suspend its execution after certain instructions if it has been scheduled for more than a timeslice period. When the current process is unable to proceed, a new current process is taken from the active set. An interrupted process is resumed as soon as all higher priority processes become unable to proceed.

2.4   Inter-process communication

Communication between processes is achieved by the use of channels. Channels between processes in the same transputer are implemented using memory locations, and channels between processes in different transputers are implemented by point-to-point links. Each link between two transputers is used solely for communication between those two transputers, and provides one occam channel in each direction.

A process can be written and compiled without knowledge of whether its channels are connected to other processes on the same transputer, or on another transputer. The same instruction sequence is used in both cases.

As in the occam model, communication takes place when both the inputting and outputting processes are ready. Consequently, the process which first becomes ready must wait until the second one is also ready. The first process is removed from the active set and its identity is stored in the channel. The processor starts to execute the next process from the active set. When the second process becomes ready, the message is transferred, and the waiting process is returned to the active set.

3 Wordlength and addressing

The instruction set is independent of the processor wordlength. Programs which manipulate bytes, words and truth values can be translated into an instruction sequence which behaves identically whatever the wordlength of the processor executing it. This results from the design of the memory addressing instructions, the use of single byte instructions, and the method of representing long operands as a sequence of prefix instructions. Differences in behaviour will come from the different word size used for arithmetic, which may result in differing overflow behaviour, and also from byte access to word arrays.

If compilers are written to produce code that does not explicitly use information about the wordlength, number of bytes per word etc., then retargetting to a transputer of a different wordlength will be much simpler. It is possible to generate code that will run on any current transputer, enabling networks of various transputers to be used without prior knowledge of their wordlengths.

3.1   Addressing

A pointer is a single word of data which identifies a byte in memory.

3.1.1   Word address and byte selector

A pointer is divided into two parts, a word address and a byte selector. The byte selector occupies the least significant bits of the word; the word address the most significant bits. The number of bits needed to represent the byte selector depends on the wordlength. (For example, 1 bit for a 16 bit machine, 2 bits for 24 or 32 bit machines, 4 bits for an 80 bit machine) . The pointer is treated as a signed value with pointer values starting from the most negative integer and continuing, through zero, to the most positive integer. This enables the standard comparison functions to be used on pointer values in the same way that they are used on numerical values. Of course, if the number of bytes in a word is a power of two, the addresses are consecutive and normal arithmetic can also be used on pointers.

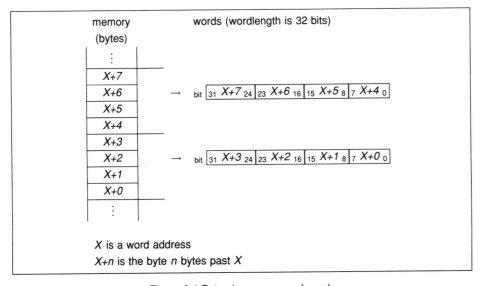

Figure 3.1 Bytes in memory and words

Certain values are never used as pointers, and are used in the implementation of communication and scheduling. These values correspond to the most negative pointer values.

In the following description, names are used to represent these and other values as follows

MostNeg   the most negative value (the most significant bit is one, and all other bits
              are zero)

MostPos   the most positive value (the most significant bit is zero, and all other bits
              are one)

NotProcess.p (= MostNeg) — used for communication and scheduling

3.2   Byte addressing

The transputer is totally 'little-endian' — i.e. less significant data is always held in lower addresses. This applies to bits in bytes, bytes in words and words in memory. Hence, in a word of data, one byte is more significant than another if its byte selector is the larger of the two. Figure 3.1 shows the ordering of bytes in words and memory for a 32 bit transputer.

4 Instruction representation

Each instruction is one byte long, and is divided into two 4 bit parts. The four most significant bits of the byte are a function code, and the four least significant bits are a data value.

bit 7 code 4 3 data 0

The representation provides for sixteen functions, each with a data value ranging from 0 to 15.

4.1   Direct functions

Research has shown that computers spend most of the time executing instructions to load and store from a small number of 'local' variables, add and compare with small constants, and jump to or call other parts of the program.

Thirteen of the functions are used to encode the most important operations performed by any computer executing a high level language. They include jumps, calls and the instructions used to access variables.

4.2   Prefix functions

Two more functions are used to allow the operand of any instruction to be extended in length.

pfix   prefix
nfix   negative prefix

All instructions begin by loading the four data bits of the instruction into the least significant four bits of the operand register which is then used as the operand of the instruction. All instructions except the prefix instructions end by clearing the operand register, ready for the next instruction.

The *pfix* instruction loads its four data bits into the operand register, and then shifts the operand register up four places. The *nfix* instruction is similar, except that it compliments the operand register before shifting it up. Consequently, a sequence of one or more prefix instructions can be placed before any instruction to extend its operand. Operands in the range −256 to 255 can be represented using one prefix instruction.

The prefix instructions have important consequences.

- Firstly, they simplify language compilation, by providing a completely uniform way of allowing any instruction to take an operand of any size up to the processor word-length.

- Secondly, they allow operands to be represented in a form independent of the word-length of the processor.

4.3   Indirect function

opr   operate

One function (*opr*) causes its operand to be interpreted as the operation code of the instruction to be executed. This selects an operation to be performed on the values held in the evaluation stack. This allows up to 16 operations to be encoded in a single byte instruction. However, the prefix instructions can be used to extend the operand of *opr*, just like any other instruction.

To ensure that programs are represented as compactly as possible, the operations are encoded in such a way that the most frequent instructions are represented without using a prefix instruction.

4.3.1   Notation

To aid clarity and brevity prefix sequences and the use of *opr* are not used in this guide. Each instruction is represented by a mnemonic, and for direct functions an item of data, which stands for the appropriate prefix sequence and function code. Also, where appropriate, an expression may be placed in a code sequence to represent the code needed to evaluate that expression.

4.4   Generating prefix sequences

Generating a prefix sequence for an operand is extremely tedious — especially when the operand is negative. Prefixing is intended to be performed by a compiler (or assembler) . Prefixing by hand is not advised!

Normally a value can be loaded into the operand register by a variety of different prefix sequences. It is clearly important to use the shortest possible sequence as this enhances both code compaction and execution speed — each prefix takes a cycle to execute. The best method of optimising object code so as to minimise the number of prefix instructions needed is shown below.

4.4.1   Prefixing a constant

The algorithm to generate a constant operand *e* for a function *op* can be quite simply described by the following recursive function.

$$prefix\ (op,\ e) = IF$$
$$e < 16\ AND\ e \geq 0$$
$$op\ (e)$$
$$e \geq 16$$
$$prefix\ (pfix,\ e \gg 4);\ op\ (e \wedge \#\ F)$$
$$e < 0$$
$$prefix\ (nfix,\ (BITNOT\ e) \gg 4);\ op\ (e \wedge \#\ F)$$

where *op* (*e*) is the byte with function code *op* and data value *e* and $\gg$ is a shift right.

4.4.2   Evaluating minimal symbol offsets

Several instructions have an operand which is the offset between the current value of **Iptr** and some other part of the code. Generating the optimal prefix sequence for the operand to one of these instructions is more complicated. This is because two, or more, instructions with offset operands can interlock so that the minimal prefix sequences for each instruction is dependent on the prefixing sequences used for the others.

For example consider the interlocking jumps below which can be prefixed in two distinct ways. The instructions

   cj +16; j −257

can be coded as

   pfix 1; cj 0; pfix 1; nfix 0; j 15

but this can be optimised to be

   cj 15; nfix 15; j 0

This is because when the two offsets are decreased by 1 their prefixing sequences take 1 byte less so that the two interlocking jumps will still transfer control to the same instructions as before. This compaction of non-optimal prefix sequences is difficult to perform and a better method is to slowly build up the prefix sequences so that the optimal solution is achieved. The following algorithm will perform this.

1. Associate with each jump instruction or offset load an 'estimate' of the number of bytes required to code it and initially set them all to 0.

2. Evaluate all jump and load offsets under the current assumptions of the size of prefix sequences to the jumps and offset loads

3. For each jump or load offset set the number of bytes needed to the number in the shortest sequence that will build up the current offset.

4. If any change was made to the number of bytes required then go back to 2 otherwise the code has reached a stable state.

The stable state that is achieved will be the optimal state.

Steps 2 and 3 can be amalgamated so that the number of bytes required by each jump is updated as the offset is calculated. This does mean that if an estimate is increased then some previously calculated offsets may have been invalidated, but step 4 will force another loop to be performed when those offsets can be corrected.

By initially setting the estimated size of offsets to zero all jumps whose destination is the next instruction are optimised out.

Knowledge of the structure of code generated by the compiler will allow this process to be performed on individual blocks of code rather than on the whole program. For example it will often be possible to optimise the prefixing in the code for the sub-components of a programming language construct before the code for the construct is optimised. When optimising the construct it will be known that the sub-components are already optimal so they can be considered as an unshrinkable block of code.

This algorithm may not be efficient for long sections of code whose underlying structure is not known. If no knowledge of the structure is available (e.g. in an assembler), all the code must be processed at once. In this case a code shrinking algorithm where in step one the initial number of bytes is set to twice the number of bytes per word is used. The prefix sequences will then shrink on each iteration of the loop. 1 or 2 iterations will produce fairly good code although this method will never produce optimal code as it will not correctly prefix the pathological example given above.

5 Sequential processes

A sequential process is executed using six registers, each one word long. The word length may be any number of bytes.

5.1   Registers

The registers are

Iptr	pointer to next instruction to be executed
Wptr	contains pointer to current process workspace
Areg	evaluation stack
Breg	evaluation stack
Creg	evaluation stack
Oreg	operand register

The **Wptr** register is used as a base from which the local variables and channels of a process can be addressed. The byte selector of the **Wptr** should always be 0.

5.1.1   Evaluation stack

Areg, **Breg** and **Creg** are organised as a three word stack. Instructions which load **Areg** first push **Breg** into **Creg** and **Areg** into **Breg**. Instructions which store **Areg** pop **Breg** into **Areg** and **Creg** into **Breg**, leaving **Creg** undefined. The effects of this are shown in figures 5.1 and 5.2.

Before				After		
		push x onto stack				
Areg	=	*a*		**Areg**	=	*x*
Breg	=	*b*		**Breg**	=	*a*
Creg	=	*c*		**Creg**	=	*b*

Figure 5.1 Effect of pushing value onto register stack

Before			After			
					a popped off stack	
Areg	=	*a*	**Areg**	=	*b*	
Breg	=	*b*	**Breg**	=	*c*	
Creg	=	*c*	**Creg**	=	*undefined*	

Figure 5.2 Effect of popping value from register stack

5.2   Local variables and constants

      ldc   load constant
      ldl   load local variable
      stl   store local variable
      ldlp load pointer to local variable
      rev   reverse

The most common operations performed by a program are loading and storing one of a small number of variables, and loading small literal values. The *ldc* instruction enables values between 0 and 15 to be loaded into the stack using a single byte instruction.

The *ldl*, *stl* and *ldlp* instruction all access locations in word addressed memory relative to the workspace pointer **Wptr**. The first 16 locations can be identified using a single byte instruction. A local variable held in workspace location *n* can be pushed onto the stack by

      ldl n

and its address can be pushed by

      ldlp n

The value of the variable can be set to a value popped from the stack by

      stl n

rev swaps the contents of **Areg** and **Breg**.

5.3   Expression evaluation

Expression evaluation is performed using the evaluation stack. The evaluation of operators with two operands is performed by instructions which combine the values of **Areg** and **Breg**. The result is left in **Areg**, and **Creg** is popped into **Breg** leaving **Creg** undefined.

Evaluation of expressions sometimes requires the use of temporary variables in the process workspace, but the number of these can be minimised by careful choice of the evaluation order.

Let *depth(e)* be the number of stack locations needed for the evaluation of expression *e*, defined by

$$
\begin{aligned}
depth(constant) &= 1 \\
depth(variable) &= 1 \\
depth(function\ call) &= \text{'infinite'} \\
depth(e1\ op\ e2) &= \text{IF} \\
&\quad depth(e1) > depth(e2) \\
&\quad\quad depth(e1) \\
&\quad depth(e1) < depth(e2) \\
&\quad\quad depth(e2) \\
&\quad \text{TRUE} \\
&\quad\quad depth(e1) + 1
\end{aligned}
$$

'infinite' should be taken as meaning greater than any finite depth. The code generation for a function call is described in a following section.

A constant expression *C* is compiled by

> *ldc C*

or by loading from a constant table as just described. A local simple variable expression *x* is compiled by

> *ldl x*

Compilation methods for non-local variables, array elements and function calls are given in later sections.

Let *commutes(op)* be *true* if *op* commutes and *false* otherwise. Let *e1* and *e2* be expressions. The evaluation of *e1 op e2* is performed by

```
IF
    depth(e2) > depth(e1)
        IF
            depth(e1) > 2
                (e2; stl temp; e1; ldl temp; op)
            commutes(op)
                (e2; e1; op)
            TRUE
                (e2; e1; rev; op)
        depth(e2) < 3
            (e1; e2; op)
        TRUE
            (e2; stl temp; e1; ldl temp; op)
```

where *(l1; l2; . . . ; ln)* represents a sequence of instructions.

In the cases where a temporary variable *temp* is required in the evaluation of *e1 op e2* to hold the value of *e2* then that variable can be used as a temporary variable in the evaluation of *e2*. Also a temporary variable used in the evaluation of *e2* and not used to hold the result of *e2* during the evaluation of e1 op e2 can be used in the evaluation of *e1*.

If it is known that all 3 registers on the register stack are available — i.e. there is not another evaluated expression already there — and *depth(e2)* is 2 then the branch

> *e2; e1; rev; op*

can be optimised by using the code

> *e1; e2; op*

removing the execution of the *rev* instruction.

5.3.1   Loading operands

All three registers of the evaluation stack are used to hold the operands of certain instructions, and the first three parameters of procedure calls. Evaluation of an operand or parameter may involve the use of more than one register. Care is needed when evaluating such operands to ensure that the first operand to be loaded is not pushed off the bottom of the register stack by the evaluation of later operands.

Three registers are available for loading the first operand, two registers for the second and one for the third. Consequently, the instructions are designed so that **Creg** holds the operand which — on average — is the

Registers required			Temp		Load seq	Instructions
C	B	A	b	a		
≤2	1	1			1	C; B; A
	1	2			2	C; A; B; rev
	1	>2			4	A; C; rev; B; rev
	2	1			1	C; B; A
	2	2		*	1	A; stl a; C; B; ldl a
	2	>2		*	1	A; stl a; C; B; ldl a
	>2	1			3	B; C; rev; A
	>2	2		*	3	A; stl a; B; C; rev; ldl a
	>2	>2		*	3	A; stl a; B; C; rev; ldl a
>2	1	1			1	C; B; A
	1	2			2	C; A; B; rev
	1	>2		*	1	A; stl a; C; B; ldl a
	2	1			1	C; B; A
	2	2		*	1	A; stl a; C; B; ldl a
	2	>2		*	1	A; stl a; C; B; ldl a
	>2	1	*		1	B; stl b; C; ldl b; A
	>2	2	*		2	B; stl b; C; A; ldl b; rev
	>2	>2	*	*	1	A; stl a; B; stl b; C;ldl b; ldl a

Table 5.1 Register loading sequences

most complex, and **Areg** the operand which is the least complex.

In some cases, it is necessary to evaluate the **Areg** and **Breg** operands in advance, and to store the results in temporary variables. This can sometimes be avoided using the reverse instruction. The following sequences may be used to load the operands A, B and C into **Areg**, **Breg** and **Creg**.

    1. *C; B; A*

    2. *C; A; B; rev*

    3. *B; C; rev; A*

    4. *A; C; rev; B; rev*

The choice of loading sequence, and of which operands should be evaluated in advance is determined by the number of registers required to evaluate each of the operands. In particular, if C requires more than two registers it must be loaded before A and B. If A or B requires more than two registers it must be evaluated before C and may need to be stored in a temporary variable if C requires more than two registers.

Table 5.1 gives the instruction sequences needed for loading three operands into the operand stack.

5.3.2   Single length signed arithmetic

Single length arithmetic with error (overflow) checking is provided by the operations

add	addition
sub	subtraction
mul	multiplication
div	division
rem	remainder

Of these, *add* and *mul* are commutative.

The instruction sequence

ldl X; ldl Y; op

where *op* is one of the arithmetic operations, evaluates the expression

X op Y

i.e. it takes the value in **Breg** as the lefthand operand and the value in **Areg** as the righthand operand.

5.3.3   Adding a constant

The instruction

adc   add constant

allows a constant value *c* to be added to **Areg** by *adc c*. Overflow is checked.

5.3.4   Single length modulo arithmetic

Single length arithmetic (with carry and overflow ignored) is provided by

sum	addition
diff	subtraction
prod	multiplication

Of these, *sum* and *prod* are commutative. However, the time taken for *prod* is proportional to the logarithm of its second (**Areg**) operand, so if *c* is a small positive constant, performance can be improved by implementing both $(c \times e)$ and $(e \times c)$ as

e; c; prod

This is particularly important when multiplication forms part of a subscript expression, as described below.

prod has been modified on the IMS T800 to give a similar fast multiplication if **Areg** is a small negative value.

5.3.5   Unary minus

The expression *(−e)* can be evaluated with overflow checked by

>   *e; not; adc 1*

or

>   *ldc 0; e; sub*

The first, using *not*, has the advantage of not needing an extra register.

The expression can be evaluated without overflow checking by

>   *ldc 0; e; diff*

5.3.6   Fractional arithmetic

Many applications, such as scientific function evaluation, currently use fixed point arithmetic. To enable this to be performed efficiently on transputers the fractional multiply instruction has been added to 32 bit transputers — i.e. the IMS T414, IMS T800 and their derivatives.

>   *fmul*   fractional multiply

fmul is a commutative arithmetic operator that interprets **Areg** and **Breg** as fixed point numbers lying in the range $-1 \leq x < 1$. The value associated with the register is 2^{-31} times its signed integer value. *fmul* returns the rounded fixed point product of these values in **Areg** and pops **Creg** up into **Breg**. The rounding is performed in *Round-to-Nearest* mode as in ANSI/IEEE 754-1985 arithmetic.

Attempting $(-1) \times_{frac} (-1)$ sets the error flag as +1 cannot be represented in this format — this is the only case in which *fmul* can overflow.

5.3.7   Logic and shifts

Bitwise operations and shifts are provided by

>   *and*   bitwise and
>   *or*   bitwise or
>   *xor*   bitwise exclusive or
>   *not*   bitwise not
>   *shl*   shift left
>   *shr*   shift right

Of these, *and*, *or* and *xor* are commutative. The *not* operation has only one operand.

The shift operations shift the operand in **Breg** by the number of bits specified in **Areg**. Vacated bit positions are filled with zero bits. The result is the initial value of **Breg** if **Areg** is zero. The instruction takes time proportional to the value of **Areg** to execute taking one cycle for every bit shifted plus a small initial overhead. The worst case can cause a transputer to 'lock' for 3 to 4 minutes. **Areg** can be checked to signal an error on out of range shifts using the *csub0* operation which is described later. The comparison instructions described later can also be used to 'short circuit' these out of range shifts so that a 0 is returned when the shift length is greater than the number of bits in a word without the actual shift instruction being executed.

5.4   Arrays and subscripts

The addressing instructions provide access to items in data structures using short sequences of single byte instructions. They also allow the representation of data structure access to be independent of the wordlength of the processor.

> *bcnt*   byte count
> *wcnt*   word count

The *bcnt* instruction multiplies **Areg** by the number of bytes in a word. It is particularly used for producing the length in bytes of a multiword data item. The *wcnt* instruction enables an address to be decomposed into its component word part and byte selector. *wcnt* takes an address in **Areg** and returns the word offset from 0 in **Areg** and the byte selector in **Breg**.

5.4.1   Forming addresses

> *ldpi*   load pointer to instruction
> *mint*   load most negative integer
> *bsub*   byte subscript
> *wsub*   word subscript

The address of a data structure held in the local workspace is loaded using the *ldlp* instruction that has already been introduced.

The address of a location in the program can be obtained by the *ldpi* operation so that relocatable code can be generated. A location which is x bytes from the byte location of the next instruction can be pushed onto the stack by

> *ldc x; ldpi*

The address of a label L: can be loaded by

> *ldc (L−M); ldpi*
> M:

The most negative address can be pushed onto the stack by *mint*. This is particularly useful for forming the address of a communication link.

Both the *bsub* and *wsub* instructions interpret **Areg** as the address of the beginning of a data structure. The result of *bsub* is the address of the byte which is **Breg** bytes from the beginning of the structure. Similarly, the result of *wsub* is the address of the byte which is **Breg** words from the beginning of the structure.

5.4.2   Structures

The 'local' operations *ldl*, *stl* and *ldlp* access word addresses relative to **Wptr**. This is useful for accessing local scalar variables. For accessing elements of structures a level of indirection is required.

Non local variable access

An element in a structure is accessed by calculating the offset of the element from the base address of that structure.

> *ldnl*   load non local variable
> *stnl*   store non local variable
> *ldnlp*   load pointer to non local variable

These 'non local' operations operate in a similar way to their 'local' counterparts except that they access a word address relative to **Areg** rather than **Wptr**. **Areg** must contain a valid word address, so its byte selector must be 0 for the instruction to be defined.

The base address in **Areg** is popped off the stack. In the case of *ldnl* and *ldnlp* the result is pushed into **Areg** replacing the original base address, while for *stnl* **Breg** is also popped out of the stack and is stored.

Access to a component of a structure can be split into two sections. Firstly the address of the component must be constructed, and then the transfer of data to or from that component must be performed.

Evaluating a subscript

Array subscripts can be evaluated efficiently using the *prod* instruction. If array A has been declared by

> $[S_1] \ldots [S_n]$ INT A:

and an access is required to

> $A[e_1] \ldots [e_n]$

then the code to evaluate the subscript is

> *ldc* S_2; e_1; *prod*; e_2; *add*; *ldc* S_3; *prod*; $\ldots$; e_n; *add*

As *prod* takes time proportional to the logarithm of the value in **Areg** the code is arranged so that the smaller operand to the *prod* is in **Areg**. This will be the actual subscript for the first *prod* but will be the subscript range for all the other times. All the array multiplications will be done in time proportional to the logarithm of the subscript size — which usually will be fairly small. There is no need for the multiplication to check for overflow as this should be checkable during compilation. Mechanisms for range checking the actual subscripts are given later.

Accessing a word addressed structure

Let *Wa* be a structure which starts at a word address and in which all component types are measured in words. Let e be a subscript expression. The address of component e of *Wa* is

> e; *Wa*; *wsub*

or

> *Wa*; *ldnlp* e

if e is a constant expression.

Accessing a byte addressed structure

Similarly, let *Ba* be a structure in which each component type is measured in bytes, and *e* a subscript expression. Then the address of component *e* of *Ba* is

  e; Ba; bsub

5.4.3   Transferring structure elements

Once the address of the structure element has been evaluated its length in bytes is required to enable it to be transferred using one of the transfer instructions.

move	move block
in	input block
out	output block

Let *Xb* be a variable or expression with length in bytes given by the value of the expression *b*. Then

  length(Xb) = b

Let *Xw* be a variable or expression of length in words given by the value of the expression *w*. Then

  length(Xw) = w; bcnt

If the value of *w*, and the target wordlength are both known to the compiler, then

  length(Xw) = ldc (w × Bytesinword)

Assignment of structures is achieved with the block move instruction *move*. It moves **Areg** bytes of data starting at address **Creg** to address **Breg**.

  v1 := v2   =   address(v2); address(v1); length(v1); move

where *address(v)* is translated as described above. The two structures must not overlap — if they do, the effect of the *move* instruction is not defined. In particular the *move* instruction can not be used to initialise a region of memory by moving from one location to an adjacent location. *move* is undefined if the value in **Areg** is negative.

Input is achieved by means of the input message instruction *in*. This transfers a communication of **Areg** bytes from channel **Breg** to address **Creg**. For example

  c ? v   =   address(v); address(c); length(v); in

Output of a variable is performed by means of the output message instruction *out*. This transfers a communication of **Areg** bytes from address **Creg** to channel **Breg**. For example

  c ! v   =   address(v); address(c); length(v); out

Both the input and output ends of a communication should have the same value in **Areg** when executing the *in* and *out* otherwise the effect of the communication is undefined.

On current transputers if different lengths are used then on an internal communication the amount of data transferred will be determined by the second process to be ready — so that if this is *out* with the longer length the message can corrupt the other process' data by overwriting. If different lengths are used on an

external communication then the process with the shorter message length will behave as if it has communicated successfully while the other process will still be waiting to finish its communication. If the length
of a communication is variable then some protocol by which the length is communicated before the actual
message is needed.

The effects of the communication instructions are undefined if the message length is negative or 0. Methods
for range and sign checking are given later.

Single word and byte transfer

The common cases of single word and byte transfer can be optimised.

Byte transfer

> *lb*   load byte
> *sb*   store byte
> *outbyte* output a single byte

lb and *sb* load and store to the byte at the address in **Areg**. *lb* replaces the address in **Areg** with the byte
value stored at that address. *sb* stores the byte value in **Breg** at the address in **Areg** and pops **Creg** up into
Areg. *outbyte* communicates the single byte in **Areg** down channel **Breg**. *outbyte* uses location (**Wptr**+0)
as a temporary variable.

So if *a* and *b* are both single byte elements and *e* is a byte valued expression then compiled code for the
transfers are

> *b := a*   =   *address(a); lb; address(b); sb*
> *b := e*   =   *e; address(b); sb*
> *c ? b*   =   *address(b); address(c); ldc 1; in*
> *c ! e*   =   *address(c); e; outbyte*

Word transfer

> *outword*   output a single word

outword communicates the single word in **Areg** down channel **Breg**. *outword* uses location (**Wptr**+0) as a
temporary variable.

So if *x* and *y* are both single word elements and *e* is a word valued expression then compiled code for the
transfers are

> *x := y*   =   *ldl y; stl x*
> *x := e*   =   *e; stl x*
> *c ? x*   =   *address(x); address(c); ldc 1; bcnt; in*
> *c ! e*   =   *address(c); e; outword*

When the target wordlength is known, channel input can be optimised as

> *address(x); address(c); ldc bytesperword; in*

5.5   Assignment

Previous sections have detailed how single assignments to variables, array elements and arrays can be compiled. The compilation of multiple assignments is more complex.

5.5.1   Multiple assignment

In occam the multiple assignment

$$V_1, \ldots , V_n := E_1, \ldots , E_n$$

is defined as being equivalent to

```
T₁ temp₁ :
  ⋮
Tₙ tempₙ :
SEQ
    PAR
        temp₁ := E₁
          ⋮
        tempₙ := Eₙ
    PAR
        V₁ := temp₁
          ⋮
        Vₙ := tempₙ
```

where the parallel separation rules of occam apply so that multiple assignments are restricted to those whose 'expanded' version is a valid occam program. $T_1 \ldots T_n$ are type definitions of the appropriate types.

Because the final assignments are performed as if in a **PAR** construct they are guaranteed not to interfere — i.e. one assignment cannot affect the destination of another — so that they can be compiled as a sequence of assignments. Hence the multiple assignment can be compiled as

$$assign(temp_1, E_1); \ldots ; assign(temp_n, E_n);$$
$$assign(V_1, temp_1); \ldots ; assign(V_n, temp_n)$$

where

$$assign(V, E)$$

represents the compiled code for

$$V := E$$

This can be optimised by re-ordering the two assignment sequences to enable registers to be used instead of some of the temporary variables.

5.6   Comparisons and conditional behaviour

Comparisons and conditional behaviour are provided by

> *eqc*   equal to constant
> *gt*   greater

together with

> *j*   jump
> *cj*   conditional jump

5.6.1   Comparison

The *eqc* instruction loads **Areg** with a truth value — *true* if **Areg** is initially equal to the instruction operand, *false* otherwise. Similarly, the *gt* instruction loads the *A* register with *true* if **Breg** > **Areg**, false otherwise. *true* and *false* are represented by 1 and 0 respectively, and therefore can be loaded with single byte load constant instructions.

It is also possible to represent *true* by a value other than 1. In particular, using

> *eqc X; not; adc 1*

and

> *gt; not; adc 1*

in place of *eqc X* and *gt* will permit −1 to be used to represent *true*.

5.6.2   Jump and conditional jump

The jump instruction, *j*, adds its operand to the address of the instruction immediately after it and puts the result into **Iptr**, thus transferring execution to another part of the program. The conditional jump instruction, *cj*, performs a jump if the value in **Areg** is 0 but otherwise pops the value in **Areg** off the register stack and continues with the next instruction. Consequently the *cj* instruction serves as 'jump if false'.

The *j* instruction will deschedule the process if the current timeslice has been exceeded, ensuring that there is an opportunity to deschedule once each time round a loop. Since a process can be descheduled by timeslicing on an unconditional jump, *j*, it is important that no information is held in the register stack at this point since if the process is descheduled the information will be corrupted by the next process that is scheduled.

The *cj* instruction never deschedules the process. The sequence

> *ldc 0; cj L*

can be used in place of

> *j L*

if it is important that descheduling does not occur. This will cause the value 0 to have been pushed onto the register stack when execution reaches *L*. This 0 value can be removed, if necessary, by making the first instruction after *L* a *diff* which will restore **Areg** and **Breg** to the values they held before the jump — however any value in **Creg** will have been lost.

5.6.3   Fast evaluation of boolean expressions

The *cj* instruction can be used to provide 'short circuit' evaluation of boolean expressions. The following table shows the correspondence between occam expressions and instructions. X and Y are expressions, and K a constant expression.

$$
\begin{array}{lcl}
\text{TRUE} & = & ldc\ 1 \\
\text{FALSE} & = & ldc\ 0 \\
\text{NOT } X & = & \neg(X) \\
X \text{ OR } Y & = & \neg(\neg(X);\ cj\ L;\ \neg(Y);\ L{:}) \\
X \text{ AND } Y & = & X;\ cj\ L;\ Y;\ L{:} \\
X = Y & = & X;\ Y;\ diff;\ eqc\ 0 \\
X <> Y & = & \neg(X;\ Y;\ diff;\ eqc\ 0) \\
X = K & = & X;\ eqc\ K \\
X <> K & = & \neg(X;\ eqc\ K) \\
X > Y & = & X;\ Y;\ gt \\
X < Y & = & Y;\ X;\ gt \\
X >= Y & = & \neg(Y;\ X;\ gt) \\
X <= Y & = & \neg(X;\ Y;\ gt)
\end{array}
$$

where

$$
\begin{array}{lcl}
\neg(\neg(X)) & = & X \\
\neg(X) & = & (X;\ eqc\ 0)
\end{array}
$$

5.6.4   Conditional transfer of control

The conditional expressions used in each conditional branch of an **IF** construct are translated as follows

$$
\begin{array}{lcl}
E & = & E;\ cj\ L; \\
P & & P;\ j\ END; \\
& L{:} &
\end{array}
$$

where the label *END:* is at the end of the code for the **IF** construct.

The compilation of a **WHILE** loop is

$$
\begin{array}{lcl}
\text{WHILE } E & = & L{:}\ \cdot \quad E;\ cj\ END; \\
P & & \qquad\quad P;\ j\ L \\
& & END{:}
\end{array}
$$

Note that this loop includes an unconditional jump. The presence of this ensures that rescheduling can take place should the loop continue for longer than a single time-slice.

5.6.5   Optimisation of conditional transfer

The following laws should be applied to the compilation of conditional expressions before code is generated to ensure that the jump is taken as early as possible.

$$
\begin{aligned}
\neg(X \text{ AND } Y)   &= \ \neg(X) \text{ OR } \neg(Y) \\
\neg(X \text{ OR } Y)   &= \ \neg(X) \text{ AND } \neg(Y) \\
(X \text{ OR } Y);\ cj\ L &= \ \neg(X);\ cj\ M;\ Y;\ cj\ L;\ M: \\
(X \text{ AND } Y);\ cj\ L &= \ X;\ cj\ L;\ Y;\ cj\ L \\
X = Y;\ cj\ L   &= \ X;\ Y;\ diff;\ cj\ L \\
X = 0;\ cj\ L   &= \ X;\ cj\ L
\end{aligned}
$$

5.6.6   Compiling CASE statements

The **CASE** statement is a special form of conditional transfer where the transfer is determined by comparing an expression to a number of constants.

When compiling the process

> **CASE** x
> $\ldots$

the expression x is evaluated and stored in a local variable by

> $x;$ stl selector

Then each branch of the **CASE** statement

> $c_1,\ \ldots\ ,\ c_n$
> P

can be compiled by

> ldl selector; ldc c_1; diff; cj L;
> ldl selector; ldc c_2; diff; cj L;
> $\ldots$
> ldl selector; eqc c_n; cj M;
> L: P; j END;
> M:

where the label *END:* is placed at the end of the **CASE** statement.

Optimised compilation of CASE

The compilation method given above will produce inefficient code for large **CASE** statements. To produce more efficient code the following rules can be used.

First build up a set of pairs of selector values and processes, consisting of every selector value in the **CASE** statement along with its associated process — the process part of each pair can be represented by the offset to the start of the compiled code for that process. Then the following rules can be used.

1. If there are 3 entries or less then use the same method as described above.

2. If there are 12 entries or less then use a binary search to limit the number of comparisons required.

3. For more than 12 entries attempt to use a jump table. The offset of the start of each selected process is placed in the table against each selector value. Entries that do not match a selector in the **CASE** statement must contain the offset of an error handler process. This jump table should be the largest table such that about $\frac{1}{3}$ of the entries are filled. This compilation strategy is then recursively called to handle the two ends. The *gcall* and *ldpi* instructions, described later, can be used to jump to the selected piece of code.

The choice of 3 or less processes, 12 or less processes and $\frac{1}{3}$ filled table are the values used in current INMOS occam compilers.

Consider compiling the **CASE** expression

$$
\begin{array}{l}
\textbf{CASE } X \\
\quad c_1 \\
\qquad P_1 \\
\quad \vdots \\
\quad c_n \\
\qquad P_n
\end{array}
$$

where, for brevity, it is assumed that all the case selectors are already in increasing order.

Three entries or less

This case is compiled as

$$
\begin{array}{l}
\textbf{IF} \\
\quad X = c_1 \\
\qquad P_1 \\
\quad \vdots \\
\quad X = c_n \\
\qquad P_n
\end{array}
$$

Four to twelve entries

This case is compiled as

$$
\begin{array}{l}
\textbf{IF} \\
\quad X <= c_{\frac{n}{2}} \\
\qquad \textbf{IF} \\
\qquad\quad X <= c_{\frac{n}{4}} \\
\qquad\qquad \dots \; etc. \\
\qquad\quad X > c_{\frac{n}{4}} \\
\qquad\qquad \dots \; etc. \\
\quad X > c_{\frac{n}{2}} \\
\qquad \dots \; etc.
\end{array}
$$

Using a jump table

Assume that $c_i \ldots c_m$ form a $\frac{1}{3}$ filled jump table. Then the case is compiled as

```
IF
    X < cᵢ
        CASE X
            c₁
                P₁
            ⋮
            cᵢ₋₁
                Pᵢ₋₁
    X > cₘ
        ... similar
    TRUE
        ... jump table code
```

where *jump table code* is

```
               X; ldc cᵢ; diff; ldc jump_size; prod; ldc (jump_table− M); ldpi
    M:         bsub; gcall;
    jump_table:
               j case_0; j case_1; ... ; j case_k
    ERROR:     ... error code
    Li:        ... code for Pᵢ

               ⋮

    Lm:        ... code for Pₘ
```

The code at *ERROR* should be the same code as used at the end of a **IF** statement where all the conditionals have been false. The *wsub*, *ldpi* and *gcall* instructions are explained in later sections.

The code at *jump_table* consists of a sequence of jump instructions which transfer control to the relevant branch *Li ... Lm* or to *ERROR*. The destination, *case_x*, of each of these jumps is *Lj* if c_j is equal to $(c_i + x)$ and is *ERROR* otherwise.

All the jumps in the *jump_table* code are prefixed to be the same length (*jump_size* bytes) to enable them to be accessed as a byte array.

5.7   Long arithmetic and shifts

5.7.1   Multiple length addition and subtraction

Signed addition and subtraction can be performed on values longer than a word using the instructions

```
    ladd    long add
    lsub    long subtract
    lsum    long sum
    ldiff   long difference
```

The *ladd* and *lsub* instructions are used for the final step of a signed multiple length addition or subtraction. The other steps can be performed using *lsum* and *ldiff*. For all four instructions, there are two unsigned single word operands held in **Areg** and **Breg**, and a carry (or borrow) operand held in the least significant bit of **Creg** (**Creg**$_{lsb}$).

The *ladd* instruction sets **Areg** to (**Breg** + **Areg**) + **Creg**$_{lsb}$. Arithmetic overflow is checked.

The *lsub* instruction sets **Areg** to (**Breg** − **Areg**) − **Creg**$_{lsb}$. Arithmetic overflow is checked.

The *lsum* instruction forms (**Breg** + **Areg**) + **Creg**$_{lsb}$ leaving the least significant word of the result in **Areg** and the most significant (carry) bit in **Breg**.

Similarly, the *ldiff* instruction forms (**Breg** − **Areg**) − **Creg**$_{lsb}$ leaving the least significant word of the result in **Areg** and the borrow bit in **Breg**.

Addition of two double length signed values with overflow checking can therefore be translated as follows

        ldc 0;
        ldl X_{lo}*; ldl* Y_{lo}*; lsum; stl* Z_{lo}*;*
        ldl X_{hi}*; ldl* Y_{hi}*; ladd; stl* Z_{hi}

Subtraction of two double length values without overflow checking is translated as

        ldc 0;
        ldl X_{lo}*; ldl* Y_{lo}*; ldiff; stl* Z_{lo}*;*
        ldl X_{hi}*; ldl* Y_{hi}*; ldiff; stl* Z_{hi}

with the final borrow left in **Areg**.

5.7.2   Multiple length multiplication and division

The long multiplication and division instructions are

        lmul   long multiply
        ldiv   long divide

The *lmul* instruction multiplies two single word unsigned operands in **Areg** and **Breg**, and adds the single word 'carry' operand in **Creg** to form a double length unsigned result. The most significant (carry) word of the result is left in **Breg**, the least significant in **Areg**. No overflow is possible so the error flag is not affected by this instruction. Multiplication of a single length unsigned value X by a double length unsigned value Y can be performed by

        ldc 0;
        ldl X; ldl Y_{lo}*; lmul; stl* Z_{lo}*;*
        ldl X; ldl Y_{hi}*; lmul; stl* Z_{hi}

which leaves the 'carry' in **Areg**.

Double length unsigned multiplication can be performed by

        ldc 0;
        ldl X_{lo}*; ldl* Y_{lo}*; lmul; stl* Z_0
        ldl X_{lo}*; ldl* Y_{hi}*; lmul; rev; stl* Z_2
        ldl X_{hi}*; ldl* Y_{lo}*; lmul; stl* Z_1*;*
        ldl X_{hi}*; ldl* Y_{hi}*; lmul; rev; stl* Z_3*;*
        ldc 0; rev; ldl Z_2*; lsum; stl* Z_2*;*
        ldl Z_3*; sum; stl* Z_3

This multiplies the two double length values X and Y to produce the quadruple length result Z. Signed multiplication can be derived from this by performing the relevant overflow checking tests on this quadruple length result before storing the bottom two words.

The *ldiv* instruction divides the double length unsigned value held in **Breg** and **Creg** (most significant word in **Creg**) by the single length unsigned value in **Areg**. The result is left in **Areg** with the remainder in **Breg**. Overflow occurs if the result cannot be represented as an unsigned single word value and causes the error flag to be set. Division of a double length value X by a single length value Y to produce a double length result Z can be performed by

> *ldc 0;*
> *ldl X_{hi}; ldl Y; ldiv; stl Z_{hi};*
> *ldl X_{lo}; ldl Y; ldiv; stl Z_{lo}*

which leaves the remainder in **Areg**.

5.7.3   Multiple length shifts

The long shift instructions are

> *lshl*   long shift left
> *lshr*   long shift right

The *lshl* and *lshr* instructions both shift the double length value held in **Breg** and **Creg** (most significant word in **Creg**) . Vacated bit positions are filled with zero bits. The number of bit positions shifted is the value of **Areg**, the result is the unshifted value if **Areg** is zero, and is undefined if **Areg** is less than zero or greater than the number of bits in a double length value. The value of **Areg** can be checked in advance by using the *csub0* instruction. The result is left in **Areg** and **Breg** (most significant word in **Breg**) .

A double length value X can be shifted Y places left by

> *ldl X_{hi}; ldl X_{lo}; ldl Y; lshl; stl X_{lo}; stl X_{hi}*

Like the single length shifts, the shift length should be checked if there is a possibility that it is greater than twice the wordlength, to prevent a transputer being 'locked' for a significant time by an 'out of range' shift.

A double length value X can be shifted Y places right with the shift length checked by the following code. This will set the error flag if the shift length is not in the range 0 .. 2 × *wordlength*.

> *ldl Y; ldc (2 × wordlength + 1); csub0;*
> *ldl X_{hi}; ldl X_{lo}; ldl Y; lshl;*
> *stl X_{lo}; stl X_{hi}*

Single length arithmetic shifts

A single length value X can be arithmetically shifted Y places right by

> *ldl X; xdble; ldl Y; lshr; stl X*

and by Y places left by

> *ldl X; xdble; ldl Y; lshl; csngl; stl X*

where *xdble* and *csgnl* are explained in a later section.

Single length rotation

A single length value X can be rotated Y places right by

   ldl X; ldc 0; ldl Y; lshr; or; stl X

and by Y places left by

   ldc 0; ldl X; ldl Y; lshl; or; stl X

If the rotate length is not guaranteed to lie in the range $0 \le Y < wordlength$ then the length should be masked with *(wordlength – 1)*. This is because the *lshl* or *lshr* will lose the bits in the word being rotated. *wordlength* can be evaluated by

   ldc 8; bcnt

bcnt multiplies the value in **Areg** by the number of bytes per word.

The long shifts can also be used to perform extraction and insertion of bit fields, even where these cross word boundaries in memory.

5.7.4   Normalising

   norm   normalise

The *norm* instruction normalises the unsigned double length value in **Areg** and **Breg** (most significant word in **Breg**) . The double length value held in **Areg** and **Breg** is shifted left until the most significant bit of the value is one. The shifted double length value remains in **Areg** and **Breg**. The number of bits shifted is left in **Creg**. If the double length value is initially zero, **Creg** is set to twice the number of bits in a word.

5.8   Integer length conversion

Conversion between signed values of different lengths can be performed using

   xword   extend to word
   cword   check word
   xdble   extend to double
   csngl   check single

5.8.1   Conversion between partword values and word values

The *xword* instruction sign extends a partword value to a single word value. The *cword* instruction checks that a single word value can be represented by a partword value. A partword value is assumed to be of any length between one bit and the number of bits in a word. It occupies the least significant bits in a word. For both instructions, the length of the partword is specified by the bit pattern of the most negative integer representable in the partword.

The two operands of the *xword* instruction are a partword in **Breg** and a length specified by **Areg**. A signed byte value can therefore be extended to a word value by

   ldc #80; xword

Similarly, the two operands of the *cword* instruction are a single word value in **Breg** and a length specified in **Areg**. The result, left in **Areg**, is the (unchanged) value of **Breg** and the error flag is set if the value cannot be represented in the partword. A signed byte value can be checked by

   ldc #80; cword

Two signed three bit values *X* and *Y* can be added and checked for overflow by

   X; ldc #4; xword;
   Y; ldc #4; xword;
   add; ldc #4; cword

5.8.2   Conversion between single word values and multiple word values

The *xdble* instruction sign extends the single length signed value in **Areg** into a double length signed value in **Areg** and **Breg** (most significant word in **Breg**) . Conversely, *csngl* reduces the double length signed value in **Areg** and **Breg** into a single length signed value in **Areg**. The error flag is set if the double length value falls outside the range of values representable in a single word.

5.9   Replication

Replicators are implemented by using the loop end instruction.

   lend   loop end

A loop is controlled by two contiguous words in memory. The first contains the value of the control variable and the second contains the unsigned number of iterations left to perform. The *lend* instruction interprets **Breg** as a pointer to such a control block and **Areg** as the number of bytes from the start of the next instruction to the start of the loop. The start of the loop normally will be before the *lend* instruction in memory so, to avoid the need for an *nfix* instruction, this offset is measured in the opposite direction from other offsets.

lend will decrement the iteration count and, if the number of iterations remaining is greater than zero, increment the control variable and subtract **Areg** from **Iptr**. If the number of iterations left after the decrement is less than or equal to zero then execution passes to the next instruction. Note that, like the jump instruction, the loop end instruction will cause rescheduling if the looping process has exceeded its timeslice , again ensuring that there is an opportunity to timeslice each time round a loop. Because of this **Creg** should not be used to hold information when *lend* is executed as, if the process is descheduled, the information will be lost.

As an example take the replicated SEQ construct. The compilation of the occam replicated SEQ is

   SEQ *i = start* FOR *count*   *start; stl i; count; stl i+1;*
        P   *ldl i+1; cj END;*
               L: *P; ldlp i; ldc (END−L); lend;*
               END:

Where it is clear that *count* is not zero the following may be used

> SEQ *i* = *start* **FOR** *count*   *start; stl i; count; stl i+1;*
>   *P*   *L:*   *P; ldlp i; ldc (END−L); lend;*
>   *END:*

The same basic instruction sequence is used to construct the loop in an occam replicated **IF**, **ALT** or **PAR**, and to initialise arrays of channels.

The count of iterations to perform should be positive. When the number of iterations is the result of an expression then it may be necessary to add some range checking to cause an error or ignore the loop if this evaluates to a negative value. If the count is negative then the loop would execute once before the *lend* instruction caused the loop to end. A negative count value should probably be treated as an error, though this depends on the definition of loops in the language being compiled.

5.10   Procedures

The instructions

> *call*   call
> *gcall*   general call
> *ajw*   adjust workspace
> *gajw*   general adjust workspace
> *ret*   return

are used to implement procedures.

The *ajw* adjusts the value of the workspace pointer by the number of words in its operand value. Workspace is claimed by using a negative value and released by using a positive value.

The *call* instruction adjusts the workspace pointer, allocating four new locations into which it stores the three evaluation stack registers and the instruction pointer — this return address is left in **Areg** by the instruction. The operand to the call is added to **Iptr** to produce the address of the procedure being called.

The *ret* instruction restores the **Iptr** and adjusts the workspace pointer to deallocate the four locations. A procedure which requires more space will normally include adjust instructions to allocate and deallocate space. When the *ret* instruction is executed any workspace claimed by the procedure should have been released so that the **Wptr** has returned to the value it held at the start of the procedure. The *ret* instruction does not affect the evaluation stack, and it is therefore possible to return up to three values to the calling procedure.

The state of the workspace after the call instruction is as shown below

		Saved values
Wptr+4	(= old **Wptr**)	
Wptr+3		**Creg**
Wptr+2		**Breg**
Wptr+1		**Areg**
Wptr+0		**Iptr**

5.10.1   Use of (Wptr+0)

The location (**Wptr**+0) is used as an extra 'register' by certain instructions. These are

>   *outword*, *outbyte*, *postnormsn*, and the instructions to implement **ALT**

Any procedure that uses one of these instructions must allocate an extra workspace slot for this use of **Wptr**+0 so that the return address is not overwritten. Workspace allocation is achieved by the *ajw* instruction.

5.10.2   Loading parameters

It is convenient to load the first three parameters of the procedure into the evaluation stack registers, and to arrange the workspace of the calling procedure so that the additional parameters can be stored in locations 0, 1, ... of the workspace before the procedure is called. In this way, the called procedure will be entered with its parameters stored in consecutive locations starting at workspace location 1. To enable the procedure to access non local variables the parameters of a procedure should include a link to the environment in which the procedure was declared.

5.10.3   The static chain

The scope rules of block structured languages can be implemented using a static chain. This involves passing a single pointer as a parameter whenever a procedure is called. The 'non local' load, store and pointer operations described in a previous section can then be used to access variables declared in an enclosing block.

Variable access via the static chain

Access via the static chain is provided by the *ldnl*, *stnl* and *ldnlp* instructions. Let n be the lexical level of the current procedure, and S_i the offset of the lexical link at level i. Then access to a location x at level $n-1$ is provided by

>   *ldl* S_n; *ldnl* x to load a variable
>   *ldl* S_n; *ldnlp* x to load a pointer to a variable
>   *ldl* S_n; *stnl* x to store a variable

Similarly, access to a location y at level $n-2$ is

>   *ldl* S_n; *ldnl* S_{n-1}; *ldnl* y
>   . . .
>   etc.

Forming a static link

When a procedure P is called, the static link for the call of P must be computed. Let n be the lexical level of the current procedure, and m the lexical level of P. If $m = n+1$ the new link is computed by *(ldlp x)* with x chosen so that P can access all of its global variables, channels etc. Otherwise the new link is computed as the value of the link location at level m. With S_i as above, this can be obtained by

```
IF
    m = n+1
       ldlp x
    m = n
       ldl Sₙ
    m = n-1
       ldl Sₙ; ldnl Sₙ₋₁
    m = n-2
       ldl Sₙ; ldnl Sₙ₋₁; ldnl Sₙ₋₂
    ...
    etc.
```

Passing the static link as a parameter

The static link for the called procedure, and the first two parameters are loaded into the evaluation stack, using a loading sequence as described above. The remaining parameters are each evaluated and stored in workspace locations starting from 0 before calling the procedure with a *call* instruction. In this way the procedure will see the return address at workspace 0, the static link at workspace 1 and the parameters at workspace 2 and onwards.

5.10.4   Other calling techniques

The *gcall* instruction enables any type of procedure call to be constructed as a sequence of instructions. Its only effect is to exchange the **Iptr** and **Areg** registers. The entry point of the procedure to be called can therefore be computed in the same way as an expression. If necessary, another *gcall* instruction can be used later to return to the calling procedure if the return address, held in **Areg**, is saved on entry to the procedure.

It is possible to compile a procedure so that it can be called using either a *call* or a *gcall* instruction. Both the *call* and *gcall* instructions leave the return instruction pointer in **Areg**. Consequently, if the first instruction in the called procedure is *(stl 0)*, the return instruction pointer will be saved in the appropriate location in the calling workspace. Of course, when using *gcall* in this way, it is necessary for the calling procedure to first adjust its workspace pointer using *(ajw −4)*, and then explicitly store the first three actual parameters in workspace locations 1, 2 and 3, as this is not be done by *gcall*. The *ret* instruction can then be used in the normal way. However, better ways of dealing with *gcall* are described below.

Efficiency will be improved if all procedures can assume they have been *call*-ed and methods similar to the ones described below are used in cases where a *gcall* is necessary. Combinations of the *call* and *gcall* instructions can be used to provide efficient implementation of procedure parameters, or for runtime linking of separately compiled procedures.

Library linkage

Most high level languages have a library system associated with them. Programs are able to make use of procedures from a library of standard procedures. To prevent the code size becoming too large the library procedures are not put into the compiled code until it is linked. This involves extracting the relevant library procedures from the libraries and 'linking' all the calls to those procedures in the compiled code to the correct address. Initially it might seem that all the code needs to be scanned for these library calls so that the link address can be instantiated but there is a simple mechanism making use of *call* and *gcall* to handle this.

Consider the compilation of a program which somewhere includes a call to the library procedure *lib_proc_1*.

Each library call is compiled into a *call* to a 'stub' at the end of the program associated with that library call. The first call to any library procedure will cause the compiler to create a stub for that procedure. A stub is a sequence of bytes into which a short piece of code will be placed by the linker so sufficiently many bytes need to be reserved for this. So between compilation and linkage the code might look like

>   . . . ;
>   *call lib_proc_1_stub;*
>   . . . ;
>   *lib_proc_1_stub:* – n bytes reserved;
>   . . .

When the program is linked the linker inserts the code

>   *j offset_to_library_procedure_code*

into the stub. Now the calls inside the program will transfer to this stub and then into the library procedure. The *j* instruction makes the code relocatable. The process might be timesliced on the *j* instruction but, since the *call* has already stored the register stack into workspace, this is not important. The parameter passing of the original *call* has been undisturbed so that the return address still points back into the program (and not to the stub) . However since the *j* instruction may be timesliced the value of **Areg** on entry to the library procedure cannot be guaranteed to be the return address. This means that library routines called by this mechanism cannot be written to be *gcall*-able. If this is required then a larger stub which explicitly adjusts the workspace, *gcall*s the library routine and then returns to its call could be used.

In scheme described above 8 bytes should be reserved for each stub on a 32 bit transputer as the offset could possibly have 32 significant bits needing 7 prefixes before the *j*. 4 bytes would be required on a 16 bit transputer. The final linked code of the example above is

>   . . . ;
>   *call lib_proc_1_stub;*
>   . . . ;
>   *lib_proc_1_stub: j offset_to_lib_proc_1;*
>   . . .

Procedure parameters

If a procedure is passed as a parameter to another procedure then calling the procedure passed as a parameter from inside the other procedure clearly needs a *gcall* instruction as the address cannot be compile time evaluated. Although this *gcall* can be made to look like a *call* by the methods above there is a more efficient way that uses a *call* to set up the parameters. Again this uses a *call* to a program stub. If the procedure parameter has n parameters then *call* the stub as if the procedure had n+1 parameters where the last parameter is the address of the procedure to be called. The stub then loads this n+1th parameter into **Areg** and performs a *gcall*. This has the same effect as a normal *call* to the procedure.

5.10.5   Other workspace allocation techniques

The *gajw* instruction exchanges the **Wptr** and **Areg** registers, allowing workspaces to be allocated dynamically, and allowing dynamic switching between existing workspaces.

If a process workspace holds a pointer to a new workspace, then

>   *ldl W*new*; gajw; stl W*old

changes to the new workspace and stores a pointer to the old workspace. The old workspace can be restored by

> $ldl\ W_{old};\ gajw$

In addition, the old workspace can be accessed using

> $ldl\ W_{old};\ ldnl\ x$
> $ldl\ W_{old};\ stnl\ x$
> $ldl\ W_{old};\ ldnlp\ x$

5.11   Functions

An occam function is a process which does not communicate, assign to any free variables — i.e. variables declared outside the process — and which returns a number of results on termination. The restriction against communication and assignment to free variables is included to ensure that functions are side effect free.

Up to 3 results whose size is less than the word length of the transputer can be returned from a function in the register stack — the *ret* instruction does not affect the registers. Further results, or results whose size is larger than the wordlength, can be returned by passing into the function the addresses of places to store these results as extra parameters.

The function

> $T_1, \ldots, T_m$ **FUNCTION** $F\ (V_1, \ldots, V_n)$
>   *local variable declarations*
>   **VALOF**
>   P
>   **RESULT** $E_1, \ldots, E_m$
> :

where, for simplicity, it is assumed that the first 3 results can be returned in registers, can be translated as

> $ajw\ -local\_variables;\ P;\ assign(result_4,E_4);\ \ldots\ ;\ assign(result_m,E_m)$
> $E_3;\ E_2;\ E_1;\ ajw\ local\_variables;\ ret$

where

> $assign(V,E)$

is the code for the assignment

> $V\ :=\ E$

and $result_4, \ldots, result_m$ are the addresses of the result stores passed as extra parameters to the function.

One of the loading sequences described earlier may be required if the expressions returned in the registers contain evaluations. Since the values returned by a multiple result function will be assigned to variables in a multiple assignment which assigns in parallel it is always possible to evaluate the results in any order. In this way cases where the results returned in the registers are not the first 3 results can be handled.

5.11.1   Calling a function

A function call must first put the addresses of the result variables in the workspace, other than the first 3 returnable in registers, followed by the parameters and the static link before calling the function. As with procedures the last three 'parameters' are placed in the register stack before the *call* instruction which automatically stores them in the workspace. When the function returns, the results whose addresses were passed will already have been stored so all that remains is to store the (up to) 3 results in the registers.

For example the function call

$$V_1, \dots, V_m := F(E_1, \dots, E_n)$$

could be compiled by

$E_3; \text{stl } 0; \dots; E_n; \text{stl } (n-3);$
$genaddr(V_4); \text{stl } (n-2); \dots; genaddr(V_m); \text{stl } ((m+n)-6);$
$E_2; E_1; \text{static\_link}; \text{call } F;$
$\text{stl } V_1; \text{stl } V_2; \text{stl } V_3$

where *genaddr(X)* is the code needed to form the address of *X*. The compiler must have already allocated sufficient workspace for the parameters that are stacked explicitly. For simplicity it has been assumed that $V_1 \dots V_3$ are all local variables whose value can be return in a register.

5.11.2   Single result functions

A function that returns a single result can be used in an expression as well as in an assignment.

A common form of function returns a single value contained in a word — the mechanism described above will return this in **Areg**. When compiling expressions the depth of such a function call should be taken as being infinite — i.e. deeper than any other form of expression. This is because the function call will always lose any other information in the registers. By giving it infinite depth the expression compilation algorithm will never call a function while another expression result is being held in a register.

5.12   Error handling

The transputer has an error flag that can be used to indicate the occurrence of an error in the execution of a process.

The instructions used for error checking are

csub0	check subscript from 0
ccnt1	check count from 1
testerr	test error flag false and clear
stoperr	stop on error
seterr	set error

5.12.1   Subscript checking

The *csub0* instruction sets error if the unsigned value of **Breg** is greater than or equal to the unsigned value of **Areg**. It can be used to check subscript operations. An expression *E* can be checked to set error if it is greater than or equal to S by

        E; S; csub0

Also

        E; mint; csub0

sets error if E is negative, and

        E; ldc 1; csub0

sets the error flag if the boolean valued expression E is *true*.

If A is an array of S words, and E an expression, then $A[E]$ can be translated into the range checked access

        E; S; csub0; A; wsub

Note that the *csub0* instruction traps both an overlarge subscript and a negative subscript, as when considered as unsigned values all negative values are greater than any positive value.

5.12.2   Checking message lengths

The *ccnt1* instruction is similar to *csub0*, but checks that the value in **Breg** is greater than 0, and less than or equal to the value in **Areg**. It can be used to check that the count of an output or input instruction is greater than zero, and less than the number of bytes in the message buffer. Also

        E; ldc 1; ccnt1

sets the error flag if the boolean valued expression E is *false*.

5.12.3   Error checking sequential processes

The *testerr* instruction loads *false* into the evaluation stack if error is set, *true* otherwise. It also clears the error flag. A sequence of instructions, S, can be checked by

        testerr; S; testerr

A form of trap handling can then be implemented by

        testerr; S; testerr; cj trap_handler

Preservation of error flag

The error flag is preserved when a priority 1 process is interrupted to enable a priority 0 process to proceed. However, the error flag is not preserved when a process is descheduled in the normal way. Consequently the sequence S above should not contain any of the following instructions

j	jump
lend	loop end
in	input message
out	output message
outword	output word
outbyte	output byte
tin	timer input
altwt	alt wait
taltwt	timer alt wait

STOP on error

The *stoperr* instruction deschedules the current process if error is set, providing graceful system degradation when execution of a process gives rise to an error. In this way parts of a system will only come to a halt when they become dependent on results from the process in which the error has occurred. A sequence of instructions, S, can be checked in this way by

> *testerr; S; stoperr*

stoperr does not affect the status of the error flag. Hence if the error flag is set then the process is descheduled and the next process in the process queue will be started with the error flag set. Because of this the error flag needs to be cleared before any error checked code to ensure that any detected error comes from that code and not a previous process.

Causing an error condition

The *seterr* instruction sets the error flag unconditionally.

5.13   Additional instructions

Two new instructions have been added on the IMS T800 to manipulate data on the main integer stack

wsubdb	form double word subscript
dup	duplicate top of stack

To enhance access to double word quantities (**REAL64**s and **INT64**s) a double word subscript instruction *wsubdb* has been added acting like *wsub* except that it indexes quantities 2 words long. Because when dealing with a double word value both words need to be accessed individually, a *dup* instruction that duplicates **Areg** in **Breg** has also been added. This can be used to duplicate an address.

In addition the *prod* instruction has been improved so that multiplying by a negative number in **Areg** takes time proportional to the most significant bit set in the absolute value of **Areg**.

6 Concurrent processes

All processes must have an area of memory reserved as their workspace — this holds the process' local variables etc. The allocation of space to concurrent processes can often be performed by a compiler, eliminating the overheads of dynamic storage allocation. However, the transputer instructions also allow fully dynamic process initiation and termination.

6.1   Workspace

A process workspace consists of a vector of words in memory. It is used to hold the local variables and temporary values manipulated by the process. The workspace is organised as a falling stack, with 'end of stack' addressing; that is the local variables of a process are addressed as positive offsets from the workspace pointer. Space is allocated and deallocated explicitly using the adjust instructions, and also by the procedure call and return instructions.

6.1.1   Special workspace locations

Some of the locations with small negative offsets from **Wptr** are used for scheduling, communication and timer input purposes. The only location which is ever likely to need to be explicitly set is location (**Wptr**−1), which is used to hold the instruction pointer of the process while it is not being executed. The other locations need to be explicitly read when analysing the state of a stopped program.

A small number of instructions — *outword*, *outbyte*, *postnormsn* and the instructions to implement **ALT** constructs — make use of (**Wptr**+0) as an extra 'register'. Processes which use these instructions must not use (**Wptr**+0) as a local variable when executing these instructions. In particular care is needed to ensure that the return address of a procedure call, which is stored at (**Wptr**+0) on entry to the procedure, is not lost.

Size of workspace

The amount of space that must be allocated in a workspace in addition to the space for the local variables is as follows. The extra locations are immediately below the address held in the workspace pointer **Wptr**. These locations are used by the scheduling mechanism to hold information about processes that are waiting or descheduled.

process with no i/o	2 words
process with only unconditional i/o using *in* and *out*	3 words
process with only unconditional i/o using *outbyte* or *outword*	3 words + (**Wptr**+0)
process with alternative input	3 words + (**Wptr**+0)
process with timer input	5 words
process with alternative timer input	5 words + (**Wptr**+0)

A process cannot use the location (**Wptr**+0) as a local variable while performing an alternative input.

6.2   Process descriptors

In order to identify a process completely it is necessary to know both its workspace address (in which the byte selector is always 0), and its priority (which is 0 or 1) . A process descriptor is the sum of the process workspace address and the process priority. The process descriptor of the current process in a transputer is held in the **Wdesc** register — **Wptr** is in fact **Wdesc** with the bottom (priority) bit masked out.

The process workspace address can be obtained from a process descriptor by forming the 'bitwise and' of the process descriptor and −2, similarly, the priority of a process is obtained by forming the 'bitwise and' of the process descriptor and 1.

6.3   Scheduling and priority

The processor can execute processes at one of two priority levels, one level for urgent (priority 0) processes, one for less urgent (priority 1) processes. A priority 0 process will always execute in preference to a priority 1 process if both are able to do so. If a priority 0 process becomes able to run whilst a priority 1 process is executing the priority 1 process is temporarily stopped — 'interrupted' — and the priority 0 process is executed. When there are no priority 0 processes able to run the interrupted process continues executing.

To minimise the time taken for an interrupting priority 0 process to start executing the following instructions are interruptable.

move	move message
input	input message
output	output message
dist	disable timer
taltwt	timer alt wait
tin	timer input

The last three of these instructions are described in the sections on alternation and timer input.

When a low priority process is interrupted by a high priority process, certain of the processor registers are written to the transputer's memory, freeing those registers for use by the high priority process. When there are no more high priority processes to be executed these registers are restored and execution of the low priority process recommences.

6.3.1   Clocks and timeslicing

The processor contains two clock registers, one for each priority. These registers start incrementing after the processor has been reset or analysed only after a store timer — *sttimer* — instruction has been executed.

The high priority clock register increments every $1\mu s$ and the low priority clock increments every $64\mu s$.

After every 1024 ticks of the high priority clock a timeslice period is said to have ended. When two timeslice period ends have occurred while the same low priority process has been continuously executing, the processor will attempt to deschedule the process. This will occur after the next *j* or *lend* instruction executed. When this happens the process is descheduled and the next waiting process is scheduled.

High priority processes are never timesliced and will run until completion, or until they have to wait for a communication.

6.3.2   Scheduling lists

The processor maintains two lists of processes which are ready to run, one for each priority level. Each ready list contains the workspaces of processes which are ready to be executed, but are not the current process — the active set. A process is started by adding it to the end of the appropriate list. When the current process is descheduled it is placed at the end of the appropriate scheduling list and the new current process is taken from the front of the list.

6.3.3   Descheduling

When a process is descheduled its **Iptr** is stored in its workspace at location (**Wptr**−1) and the process is added to the relevant scheduling list. **Areg**, **Breg** and **Creg** are not saved when a process is descheduled because of timeslicing or waiting for a communication. This means that a process must not attempt to transfer any information in the evaluation stack across instructions that can be timesliced or across any communication instruction. If the process is descheduled other processes will corrupt the stack before it is rescheduled.

6.3.4   Interruption

When a high priority process becomes ready while a low priority process is executing the low priority process is interrupted. The **Iptr**, **Wptr**, **Areg**, **Breg** and **Creg** are all stored in special locations at the bottom of the memory map and the high priority process starts to execute. At the next point where there are no high priority processes able to execute the saved values of the registers are reloaded and execution of the low priority process continues. There can only ever be at most one interrupted process. Note that an interrupted process is not placed onto the scheduling lists.

6.4   Initiation and termination

Initiation and termination of concurrent process can be performed by

>   *startp*   start process
>   *endp*   end process

6.4.1   Starting a concurrent process

The *startp* instruction initiates a new concurrent process at the same priority as the current process. **Breg** should contain the offset from the end of the current instruction to the first instruction of the new process. **Areg** should be the address of a workspace for the new process — this must be a word address.

6.4.2   Terminating a concurrent process

The *endp* instruction terminates the current process. **Areg** should contain the workspace address of a specific successor process which continues only after a number of concurrent processes have all terminated. Usually, the workspace of the successor process is the same as the workspace of the process which started the other concurrent processes.

The first word in the workspace of the successor process (**Wptr**$_{succ}$+1) is used to hold a count of the number of concurrent processes which have still to terminate before the successor process continues. The zeroeth (**Wptr**$_{succ}$+0) word contains the **Iptr** at which the successor process will start to execute. This count word must be initialised prior to initiation of the concurrent processes as should the word containing the successor process **Iptr**.

6.5   Compiling PAR

The occam process

```
    PAR
        P
        Q
        R
```

can therefore be translated as follows

```
            ldc 3; stl 1;
            ldc (L5–L6); ldpi;
    L6:     stl 0;
            ldc (L1–L2); ldlp WP;
            startp;
    L2:     ldc (L3–L4); ldlp WQ;
            startp;
    L4:     R; ldlp 0; endp;
    L1:     P; ldlp – WP; endp;
    L3:     Q; ldlp – WQ; endp;
    L5:
```

where *WP* is the offset from the workspace of *R* to that of *P*, and *WQ* is the offset from the workspace of *R* to that of *Q*. There are only two *startp* instructions as the process that executes the **PAR** continues as process R. In this way the **PAR** construct is treated as a process that spawns one, or more, concurrent 'subprocesses' and synchronises on termination.

6.6   Other scheduling instructions

```
        runp    run process
        stopp   stop process
        ldpri   load priority
```

The *runp* instruction starts a process. **Areg** should contain the process descriptor of an existing process — i.e. should point to a workspace in which location −1 contains the value to be loaded into **Iptr** when the process is scheduled. *runp* can be used to start a process at either priority level by setting or clearing the bottom bit in the process descriptor in **Areg**.

The *stopp* instruction simply stops the current process saving the value of **Iptr** in the workspace. The process is not put onto the scheduling lists so to restart it a *runp* instruction is needed.

The *ldpri* instruction loads the priority of the current process into the evaluation stack.

If *I* is a variable holding the address of the first instruction of a new process, and *W* holds the address of a workspace for the process, then

```
        ldl I; ldl W; stnl – 1; ldl W; ldpri; or; runp
```

will start the process at the current priority.

Similarily

       ldl l; ldl W; stnl − 1; ldl W; runp

will start the process at high priority.

6.7   PRI PAR

The **PRI PAR** construct allows two processes to be run concurrently with the first having priority 0 and the second priority 1. This should only be used from low priority processes to prioritise certain subprocesses, as otherwise a high priority process will split into two process with one being run at low priority. Compile time checking should be used to ensure that any use of prioritisation is valid. In particular checking should be performed to prevent **PRI PAR**s being nested. It is often possible to ensure that prioritisation is used validly by restricting the use of **PRI PAR** to the outermost level of a program.

The construct

```
PRI PAR
   P
   Q
```

runs processes P and Q concurrently with P at priority 0 and Q at priority 1. It should only be executed from a priority 1 process. The following code will implement this

```
       ldc 2; stl 1;
       ldc (L3−L4); ldpi;
L4:    stl 0;
       ldc (L1−L2); ldpi;
L2:    ldlp (WP−1); stnl 0;
       ldlp WP; runp;
       Q; ldlp 0; endp;
L1:    P; ldlp −WP; endp;
L3:    ldlp 0; ldc 1; or; runp; stopp
```

The differences between this and the unprioritised **PAR** are that process P is started at high priority by explicitly storing its instruction pointer in the workspace and then running it using a *runp*. In addition some extra code appears at the end. This is because the priority of the process restarting at *L3:* is determined by the process of the **PRI PAR** that terminated last. The code at *L3:* explicitly sets itself to low priority. The *runp* instruction in effect starts a second version of the process at low priority and then the *stopp* removes the first version which has unknown priority. When the *runp* is executed there is no instruction pointer in the workspace but this is placed there by the *stopp*.

6.8   Channels and communication

A channel is used to allow two processes to synchronise and communicate. Channel synchronisation may be implemented either by a word in memory (for communication within a transputer) or by a serial link (for communication between transputers) .

All channels have an address associated with them. For link channels these are defined to be certain reserved addresses. For channels handling communication between processes on the same transputer a memory location must be allocated by the compiler.

The instructions used for communication are the same, regardless of whether the channel is implemented using a memory location or using a serial link; the channel address being used by the processor to determine what action is performed. This allows a procedure to be compiled without knowledge of whether its parameter channels are implemented by memory locations or by serial links.

6.8.1   Initialising channels

Before a memory location can be used as a channel, it must be initialised to the special value *NotProcess.p*. This value can be obtained by the *mint* instruction. It is convenient to do this when a channel declaration is executed. For example

        CHAN OF *PROTOCOL c* :   *mint; stl c*

        [n] **CHAN OF** *PROTOCOL c* :   *ldc 0; stl i; ldc n; stl i+1;*
                                      L: *mint; ldl c; ldl i;*
                                           wsub; stnl 0;
                                         ldlp i; ldc (END−L); lend;
                        END:

The *input* and *output* instructions use the memory location to provide synchronised communication between two concurrent processes, as defined by occam. After each communication, the store location returns to its initial value, *NotProcess.p.*

6.9   Time

Time is cyclic. There are two clock registers, one for each priority level, **ClockReg$_0$** and **ClockReg$_1$**. The high priority clock **ClockReg$_0$** increments every 1μs. The low priority clock **ClockReg$_1$** increments every 64μs. Whenever **ClockReg** = *MostPos*, it is 'incremented' to *MostNeg*.

6.9.1   Past and future

For each priority level all times which are between *(***ClockReg** *PLUS 1)* and *(***ClockReg** *PLUS MostPos)* are considered to be in the future and those which are between *(***ClockReg** *PLUS MostNeg)* and **ClockReg** are considered to be in the past.

The AFTER relation

Care is needed when operating on cyclic quantities such as time. The usual 'greater than' relation is replaced by the relation **AFTER** which is defined by

        $(x\ \textbf{AFTER}\ y) \equiv ((x - y) > 0)$

and can be translated into

        x; y; diff; ldc 0; gt

The usual transitive property does not hold for the after relation, that is:

        $(x\ \textbf{AFTER}\ y) \wedge (y\ \textbf{AFTER}\ z)$ does not imply $(x\ \textbf{AFTER}\ z)$

A consequence of this property of cyclic time is that a group of times are only unambiguous if they are all contained within a half cycle.

6.9.2   Reading the clock

> *ldtimer*   load timer

The current value of the processor clock can be read by executing a 'load timer' instruction *ldtimer*. This reads the value of the high priority clock when executed in a high priority process and the low priority clock when executed in a low priority process.

6.9.3   Timer input

A process can arrange to perform a 'timer input', in which case it will become ready to execute after a specified time has been reached.

> *tin*   timer input

The timer input instruction, *tin*, requires a time to be supplied in **Areg**. If this time is in the 'past' — i.e. **ClockReg AFTER Areg** — then the instruction has no effect. If the time is in the 'future' — i.e. **Areg AFTER Clockreg** or **Areg = ClockReg** — then the process is descheduled. When the specified time is reached the process is scheduled again. The process may not start to execute immediately, as other processes may already be waiting on the scheduling list. Consequently when the process starts to execute, the value in the clock may be some time after the time specified in the timer input.

For example the following code sequence executed in a low priority process would cause the process to be descheduled for (at least) one second by waiting for $1000000 \div 64 (= 15625)$ ticks of the clock.

> *ldtimer; ldc 15625; sum; tin*

Note that when dealing with time the unsigned modulo arithmetic operations *sum*, *diff*, must be used rather than *add* and *sub* which would cause an arithmetic overflow when the value representing the time wrapped round from *MostPos* to *MostNeg*.

6.10   Alternative input

The **ALT** construct in occam allows a process to make a choice over its future behaviour dependent on the readiness of other concurrent processes to communicate with it. Several instructions are used to implement this construct.

6.10.1   Components of an alternation

An alternation selects one of its component alternatives. Each component may have one of the following forms where *e* is a boolean expression

skip guard		*e* **& SKIP** *P*
channel guard	*c ? v* *P*	*e* **&** *c ? v* *P*
timer guard	*timer* ? **AFTER** *t* *P*	*e* **&** *timer* ? **AFTER** *t* *P*

An alternation is translated by translating each component alternative into a sequence of instructions to be performed when one of its component alternatives is selected, and a sequence of instructions to select one of the component alternatives.

6.10.2   Selection of alternatives

The selection of the alternative is performed by an alt start instruction, a sequence of enable instructions (one for each alternative), an alt wait instruction, a sequence of disable instructions (one for each alternative) and an alt end instruction. The sequence in which the alternatives are enabled is unimportant, but the sequence in which they are disabled determines the priority of the alternatives. The first ready alternative to be disabled is selected.

The instructions used to implement the alternative are

alt	alt start
altwt	alt wait
altend	alt end
talt	timer alt start
taltwt	timer alt wait

Workspace pointer during selection

The workspace pointer of the process must not change between the execution of the alt start instruction and the corresponding alt end instruction. The location (**Wptr**+0) has a special use, and is not preserved over the disabling sequence (from the alt wait instruction to the alt end instruction) . In addition various locations at small negative offsets from **Wptr** are used during the execution of an alternative.

Timer alternatives

An alternation which does not contain a timer alternative can be implemented using the *alt* and *altwt* instructions; one which contains timer alternatives must use the *talt* and *taltwt* instructions.

Each alternative guard is translated into an enable instruction and a corresponding disable instruction. The enable and disable instructions are

enbs	enable skip
diss	disable skip
enbc	enable channel
disc	disable channel
enbt	enable timer
dist	disable timer

An enable instruction expects the boolean component of the guard to be passed in **Areg**. The channel or time component of the guard for an enable channel or enable timer instruction is passed in **Breg**. If the boolean in **Areg** is *true* then that guard is 'enabled'. The value of the boolean remains in **Areg** at the end of the instruction.

For disable instructions **Areg** should contain an offset from the start of the instruction following the *altend* to the start of the code for that branch of the alternative. The boolean component of the guard is passed in **Breg**. The channel or time component of the guard for a disable channel or disable timer instruction is passed in **Creg**. The instruction returns a boolean in **Areg** which is *true* only if that branch of the alternative is the one to have been selected.

6.10.3   Translation of alternatives

The translation of alternatives is as follows. Guards which do not have a boolean conjunct to them have
TRUE & added.

$$c ? v \qquad\quad = \quad \textbf{TRUE \&}\ c ? v$$
$$\quad P \qquad\qquad\qquad\quad P$$

$$timer\ ?\ \textbf{AFTER}\ t\ =\ \textbf{TRUE \&}\ timer\ ?\ \textbf{AFTER}\ t$$
$$\quad P \qquad\qquad\qquad\qquad P$$

Guards are enabled and disabled by the following sequences of instructions

	enable	disable
e & **SKIP** *P*	*e; enbs*	*e; L; diss*
e & *c* ? *v* *P*	*c, e, enbc*	*c; e; L; disc*
e & *timer* ? **AFTER** *t* **P**	*t, e, enbt*	*t; e; L; dist*

where *L* is the offset between the alt end instruction and the start of the instruction sequence corresponding
to process *P*. The process *P* is translated as

$$e\ \&\ \textbf{SKIP} \qquad\quad = \quad P; j\ END$$
$$\quad P$$

$$e\ \&\ c\ ?\ v \qquad\qquad = \quad c\ ?\ v;\ P;\ j\ END$$
$$\quad P$$

$$e\ \&\ timer\ ?\ \textbf{AFTER}\ t\ =\ P;\ j\ END$$
$$\quad P$$

where *END* labels the instruction following the alternative process.

6.10.4   Compiling an ALT statement

Using the enabling and disabling sequences given above, an **ALT** statement of the form

$$\textbf{ALT}$$
$$\quad G_0$$
$$\qquad P_0$$
$$\quad \vdots$$
$$\quad G_n$$
$$\qquad P_n$$

translates into

```
              alt;
              enable(G₀); ... ; enable(Gₙ);
              altwt;
              disable(G₀); ... ; disable(Gₙ);
              altend
        END:
```

where *talt* and *taltwt* would need to be used if any of the guards G_i was a timer guard.

6.10.5   Trapping degenerate alternatives

It is possible for all the guards of an alternative to fail due to all the boolean components being *false*. In some circumstances this might need to be reported as an error. Each enable instruction terminates with the value of its boolean expression in **Areg**. This can be used during the enabling sequence to detect whether the boolean expressions in all the alternatives are false. For example

```
        alt;
        enable(G₀); stl F;
        enable(G₁); ldl F; or; stl F;
        ⋮
        enable(Gₙ); ldl F; or; ldc 1; ccnt1;
        altwt
```

Where the *ccnt1* instruction will set the error flag if the disjunct of all the boolean components is *false*. This uses the temporary local variable *F* to evaluate the disjunct. If it is known that none of the enabling sequences can cause the process to be descheduled, and the evaluation of the two operands to the enable requires no more than two registers, then the following sequence could be used

```
        alt;
        enable(G₀);
        enable(G₁); or;
        ⋮
        enable(Gₙ); or; ldc 1; ccnt1;
        altwt
```


6.10.6   Replicated ALT

```
        ALT i = b FOR c
          G
            P
```

The enabling sequence for a replicated **ALT** involves using a loop round the enable guard instructions as described earlier.

The disabling sequence for a replicated **ALT** is more complex as the value of the control variable *i* for the branch selected must be passed into the execution of *P*. Each disable instruction terminates with **Areg** holding *true* if the alternative was selected and *false* otherwise. This allows the disabling sequence for a replicated alternative to record the selected value of the control variable. The disabling sequence for *G* is

```
        disable(G); cj M; ldl i; stl selected_i; M:
```

where the process *P* will use *selected_i* as the constant *i*.

7 Floating point arithmetic

This chapter explains how floating point arithmetic can be implemented efficiently on a transputer. Most of the contents deal with the instruction set of the floating point unit on the IMS T800 floating point transputer. Floating point arithmetic can be implemented efficiently in software on the IMS T414 and IMS T212. The last section details some instructions on the IMS T414 designed to enhance floating point performance.

The ANSI/IEEE 754 floating point arithmetic standard

INMOS implementations of floating point arithmetic are designed to conform to the requirements of the ANSI/IEEE 754-1985 floating point arithmetic standard. Familiarity with the general concepts of the IEEE 754 standard is helpful to understand some of the more detailed areas of the floating point unit — but it is by no means essential. Copies of the IEEE 754 standard can be obtained from,

The Secretary,
IEEE Standards Board,
345 East 47th Street,
New York, NY 10017,
U.S.A.

7.1 Overview of the IMS T800

To enhance the performance of transputers on applications using floating point arithmetic, a floating point transputer, the IMS T800, has been developed. This has an on chip floating point unit to handle the floating point arithmetic. The floating point unit only affects compilation of floating point code. All the information about programming high level language constructs given in earlier sections is still valid and explains how the control and data structures can be programmed.

The transputer instruction set has been extended by adding secondary operations to perform the floating point instructions. These instructions can be viewed as being executed by the main processor on the transputer. In reality they are executed in the floating point unit which runs concurrently with the main processor. The floating point unit adds a three deep floating point stack to complement the three deep integer stack of the main processor. These floating point registers can contain either **REAL32** or **REAL64** values.

The addresses of floating point values are formed on the main processor stack, and values are transferred between the addressed memory locations and the floating point unit stack under the control of the main processor. As the main processor stack is only used to hold addresses of floating point values, the word length of the main processor is independent of that of the floating point unit — consequently, it would be possible to use the same floating point unit together with, for example, a 16 bit processor such as the IMS T212 transputer.

7.1.1 Concurrent operation of the floating point unit

Although a floating point transputer can be treated as a single processor that performs both integer and floating point arithmetic, some knowledge of the concurrency between these two processors is needed to obtain the highest performance from the transputer.

A floating point transputer consists of two processors running concurrently. One is a standard processor almost identical to a non floating point transputer such as the IMS T414. The other is a high performance floating point processor. Points in an instruction stream where data needs to be transferred to or from the floating point unit are called synchronisations. At synchronisations the first processor ready will wait until the second is ready at which point the data transfer will take place and both will be able to proceed concurrently again. This can be modelled in occam as two parallel processes communicating via channels.

```
CHAN OF ANY to.fpu, from.fpu :
PAR
    [memsize]INT memory :
    INT Areg, Breg, Creg :
    ... 'code' for integer cpu

    REAL FAreg, FBreg, FCreg :
    ... 'code' for floating point unit
```

To obtain the maximum performance from a floating point processor it is important to minimise the number of times where the main cpu is waiting for the floating point unit to synchronise and vice versa. If possible this time should be used for some useful purpose such as computing the address of the next variable to be accessed. If code is generated carefully it is often possible to totally overlap the address generation of variables - even in 2 or 3 dimensional arrays - with the previous calculation so that the speed of execution is not hampered by the data structure access. Simple compile time mechanisms to aid this overlapping are described later.

7.1.2   Floating point unit instructions

Instructions are provided to perform floating point arithmetic on the floating point unit. All these instructions have names beginning with *fp*. These instructions allow floating point values to be transferred from memory to the floating point unit and vice versa, and to manipulate values on the floating point unit evaluation stack.

Floating point unit microcode indirection

To economise on the microcode, certain floating point instructions are selected by a value held in **Areg**

        fpentry   floating point unit entry

fpentry uses the value held in **Areg** as an entry point into the microcode ROM on the floating point unit. The instructions that are listed in the floating point instruction list that follows as having length 'seq' are executed by loading their instruction code into **Areg** then performing a *fpentry*. However, as this only really affects the code generator in a compiler, in the next sections the use of *fpentry* is omitted and those instructions will be represented by their entry point mnemonic only. When allocating registers the need to use **Areg** to execute certain instructions has to be taken into account. The names of the operations that use *fpentry* start with *fpu* so the code represented by

        fpuname

is

        ldc fpuname; fpentry

7.2   Registers

In addition to the three deep stack of integer registers in the standard transputer — **Areg**, **Breg** and **Creg** — the floating point unit contains another three deep stack — **FAreg**, **FBreg** and **FCreg**. Each floating point register can hold either a **REAL32** or a **REAL64** and has an internal flag associated with it to signify the length of the data it contains. The floating point stack behaves in a similar manner to the integer stack. When a value is loaded in **FAreg** the values in **FAreg** and **FBreg** are pushed down into **FBreg** and **FCreg** respectively. When a value is stored from **FAreg** **FBreg** is popped up into **FAreg** and **FCreg** into **FBreg**.

Areg =	a	FAreg =	fa	(Wptr+5) : X
Breg =	b	FBreg =	fb	
Creg =	c	FCreg =	fc	
		ldlp 5		
Areg =	Wptr+5	FAreg =	fa	
Breg =	a	FBreg =	fb	
Creg =	b	FCreg =	fc	
		fpldnlsn		
Areg =	a	FAreg =	X	
Breg =	b	FBreg =	fa	
Creg =	undefined	FCreg =	fb	

Figure 7.1 Stack use in floating point load

The **REAL32** and **REAL64** formats supported are the single and double precision formats as specified in the IEEE 754 standard.

Two instructions are provided to directly manipulate the floating point stack.

      fpdup   duplicate top of floating point stack
      fprev   reverse top of floating point stack

fpdup copies **FAreg** into **FBreg** and pushes the old value of **FBreg** into **FCreg**. *fprev* swaps **FAreg** and **FBreg**.

7.3   Loading floating point values

      fpldnlsn   load non local single length floating point number
      fpldnldb   load non local double length floating point number
      fpldnlsni load indexed single length floating point number
      fpldnldbi load indexed double length floating point number

Floating point values are loaded from memory into the floating point stack by loading a pointer to the **REAL32** or **REAL64** into **Areg** then executing the *fpldnlsn* or *fpldnldb* instruction respectively. The floating point registers push down when a new value is loaded in the same way as on the main register stack. The main stack is popped to remove the pointer **Areg**.

REAL64s are stored in memory in two words with the least significant word at the lower address. When loading (or storing) a **REAL64** the pointer placed in **Areg** points to the lower word of the two.

For example to load the contents of (**Wptr**+5) as a **REAL32** value onto the floating point stack the code sequence below is used.

      ldlp 5; fpldnlsn

The state of the two stacks during this sequence is shown in figure 7.1.

Accessing floating point vectors is done in a similar way to that used for integer vectors. To load the **REAL64**

Areg =	*a*	**FAreg** =	*fa*	(**Wptr**+7) : *x*
Breg =	*b*	**FBreg** =	*fb*	(**Wptr**+8) : *y*
Creg =	*c*	**FCreg** =	*fc*	
		ldlp 7		
Areg =	**Wptr**+7	**FAreg** =	*fa*	
Breg =	*a*	**FBreg** =	*fb*	
Creg =	*b*	**FCreg** =	*fc*	
		fpstnldb		
Areg =	*a*	**FAreg** =	*fb*	(**Wptr**+7) : *lower 32 bits of fa*
Breg =	*b*	**FBreg** =	*fc*	(**Wptr**+8) : *top 32 bits of fa*
Creg =	*undefined*	**FCreg** =	*undefined*	

Figure 7.2 State of stacks in floating point store

X[e] the following sequence can be used

> *e; ldlp X; wsubdb; fpldnldb*

This example uses the *wsubdb* instruction that has been added to ease access to arrays of the double word values — **REAL64** and **INT64**.

To aid code compactness in array access, two indexed floating point loads are provided.

> *fpldnlsni*   =   *wsub; fpldnlsn*
> *fpldnldbi*   =   *wsubdb; fpldnldb*

7.4   Storing values

> *fpstnlsn*   store single length floating point number non local
> *fpstnldb*   store double length floating point number non local

The address for storing values is created in the same way as for loading. The floating point store instructions take the contents of **FAreg** and store it at the location pointed to by **Areg**. Both stacks are popped up to remove the data that has just been used. The compiler is expected to ensure that single length data is stored with a *fpstnlsn* and double length with a *fpstnldb*. The floating point unit makes no check on the correctness of the length and the behaviour of mismatched stores is undefined — the compiler should prevent this from happening.

The following code fragment stores the **REAL64** value in **FAreg** to the word address (**Wptr**+7) — n.b. the double word value will be stored in (**Wptr**+7) and (**Wptr**+8) .

> *ldlp 7; fpstnldb*

The state of the two stacks during this sequence is shown in figure 7.2.

Storing to arrays is the same as for loading except that there are no store indexed instructions. To store into arrays the following code sequences are used.

> *e; ldlp X; wsub; fpstnlsn*
> *e; ldlp X; wsubdb; fpstnldb*

7.5   Expressions

7.5.1   Arithmetic operations

> *fpadd*   floating point addition
> *fpsub*   floating point subtraction
> *fpmul*   floating point multiplication
> *fpdiv*   floating point division

Each of these operations evaluates **FBreg** *op* **FAreg** leaving the result in **FAreg** and popping **FCreg** up into **FBreg** like the integer arithmetic operations.

Since the length of values is stored with the registers on the floating point stack there is no need for separate single and double length arithmetic instructions. The arithmetic instructions all return the correct result as defined by the IEEE 754 standard. The arithmetic instructions assume both operands are of the same format — if not the result is undefined — and this should be taken care of by the type checking in a high level language. By default all rounding carried out on the floating point unit is *Round-to-Nearest*.

The remainder and square root operations required by the IEEE standard are provided by code sequences detailed later.

7.5.2   Floating point rounding mode

> *fpurn*   set round mode to *Round-to-Nearest*
> *fpurz*   set round mode to *Round-to-Zero*
> *fpurp*   set round mode to *Round-to-Plus-Infinity*
> *fpurm*   set round mode to *Round-to-Minus-Infinity*

In addition to the default *Round-to-Nearest*, the other three rounding modes in the IEEE standard are provided.

The floating point rounding mode is reset at the end of all other floating point instructions to *Round-to-Nearest*. In this way other rounding modes must be explicitly set before each operation when required. If there is no explicit selection of a rounding mode then the mode will be *Round-to-Nearest*. This mechanism avoids the need to store the rounding mode of a process on timeslicing so that the process switching time is not affected.

To use any other rounding mode the rounding instruction should be immediately preceded by a set rounding instruction. *Round-to-Zero* mode provides truncation rounding, while the *Round-to-Plus-Infinity* and *Round-to-Minus-Infinity* modes have their use in interval arithmetic.

7.5.3   Compiling floating point expressions

Compilation of expressions to be evaluated on the floating point stack can be done in much the same way as for integer expressions. The depth of stack needed to evaluate an expression is given by

$$
\begin{aligned}
depth(constant) &= 1 \\
depth(variable) &= 1 \\
depth(function\ call) &= \text{'infinite'} \\
depth(e1\ op\ e2) &= \text{IF} \\
&\quad depth(e1) > depth(e2) \\
&\qquad depth(e1) \\
&\quad depth(e1) < depth(e2) \\
&\qquad depth(e2) \\
&\quad \text{TRUE} \\
&\qquad depth(e1) + 1
\end{aligned}
$$

An expression that is a variable X is evaluated by

> X; *fpldnlsn* — for single length X
> X; *fpldnldb* — for double length X

An expression that is a constant C is best evaluated by the compiler storing the value of C in a constant table *Constants* at position *Constant$_C$* then using the following code

> *ldlp Constants; ldnlp Constant$_C$; fpldnlsn* — for single length
> *ldlp Constants; ldnlp Constant$_C$; fpldnldb* — for double length

An expression *e1 op e2* is evaluated by

```
IF
    depth(e2) > depth(e1)
        IF
            depth(e1) > 2
            (e2; ldlp temp; fpstnl; e1; ldlp temp; fpldnl; op)
            commutes(op)
            (e2; e1; op)
            TRUE
            (e2; e1; fprev; op)
    depth(e2) < 3
        (e1; e2; op)
    TRUE
        (e2; ldlp temp; fpstnl; e1; ldlp temp; fpldnl; op)
```

Where *fpstnl* and *fpldnl* here stand for either the single or double length load or store instruction depending on the type of the value being placed in a temporary variable.

When all three registers are known to be available and *depth(e2)* is 2 then the code

> *e2; e1; fprev; op*

can be optimised to

> *e1; e2; op*

When **FAreg** and **FBreg** need to be loaded with specific values — e.g. for a comparison — then code sequences similar to those given in the section on loading integer operands can be used. The loads, stores and reverses will need to be modified in a similar way to the modifications made to the expression compiler above.

7.5.4   Remainder and square root

Remainder and square root are provided as code sequences. Both these operations take much longer than other instructions to complete. In particular they take longer than the interrupt latency period of the IMS T414. The mechanism of making certain instructions — e.g block move — on the transputer interruptable could not easily be extended to these cases. Instead the solution has been to break the instruction up into a sequence of component instructions each of which completes within the desired interrupt latency period.

These instructions are designed solely for the purposes of building the remainder and square root operations. They have no other intended use and should not be used outside the following code sequences. The effect of any other use is undefined and in the case of *fpremstep* may fail to terminate. In particular they **cannot** be used to generate fast but less accurate results.

Square root

> *fpusqrtfirst*   first step of square root
> *fpusqrtstep*   intermediate step of square root
> *fpusqrtlast*   last step of square root

Unlike the other arithmetic operations there are different versions of square root for single and for double length. If rounding other than *Round-to-Nearest* is required the rounding mode should be set immediately before the *fpsqrtlast* instruction. Each instruction sequence evaluates the square root of **FAreg** and leaves the result in **FAreg**. **FBreg** and **FCreg** are used during the evaluation so their initial values are destroyed. 2 square root steps — *fpusqrtstep* — are need in a single length square root evaluation and 5 for double length.

The code sequence for a single length square root in *Round-to-Nearest* mode is

> *fpusqrtfirst; fpusqrtstep; fpusqrtstep; fpusqrtlast*

and for double length in *Round-to-Zero* mode

> *fpusqrtfirst; fpusqrtstep; fpusqrtstep; fpusqrtstep; fpusqrtstep; fpusqrtstep; fpurz; fpusqrtlast*

Remainder

> *fpremfirst*   first step of remainder
> *fpremstep*   loop step of remainder

The code to implement remainder is

```
          fpremfirst;
          eqc 0;
          cj next;
loop:     fpremstep;
          cj loop;
next:
```

This evaluates **FBreg** REM **FAreg** and leaves the result in **FAreg**. Remainder produces an exact result so needs no rounding mode. It also makes use of all registers so that any value initially in **FCreg** will be lost. As each remainder instruction pushes a boolean into **Areg** to control the looping with the *cj*, any values in the integer stack must be assumed to be destroyed by the remainder sequence.

7.5.5   Floating point argument reduction

Most algorithms used to calculate standard functions — such as the trigonometric functions — are implemented by range reducing the argument into a primary range in which there is a well behaved polynomial approximation. The range reduction usually takes the form of taking the remainder of the argument by the periodicity of the function. For example if the approximation for sine were defined over $[-\pi, \pi]$ then the following reasoning would allow $\sin x$ to be evaluated.

$$\forall n : \mathbf{Z}. \, y : [-\pi, \pi]. \sin y = \sin(2n\pi + y)$$
$$\wedge \, \exists m : \mathbf{Z}. \, r : [-\pi, \pi].(x = m \times 2\pi) + r \wedge (r = x \text{ REM } 2\pi)$$
$$\Rightarrow \sin x = \sin(x \text{ REM } 2\pi)$$

So an occam implementation of sine where *SINEPRIM* was a function that evaluated sines over $[-\pi, \pi]$ could be

```
REAL32 FUNCTION SINE (VAL REAL32 X)
   VAL REAL32 Two.Pi IS 6.283185307 (REAL32) :
   REAL32 Reduced.X :
   VALOF
      Reduced.X := X REM Two.Pi
      RESULT SINEPRIM (Reduced.X)
```

However in practice the value of 2π that would be used would not be exact. As m increased this error in 2π would be reflected in an increasingly large error in *Reduced.X* — i.e. the value used in the primary range calculation would become inaccurate. Suppose in this example that the value π_{REAL32} is used to derive *Two.Pi* where

$$\pi_{REAL32} = \pi + \epsilon$$

Then when reducing the range of X obtain the value *Reduced.X* with

$$
\begin{aligned}
Reduced.X &= X - m \times Two.Pi \\
&= X - m \times 2 \times \pi_{REAL32} \\
&= X - 2m \times (\pi + \epsilon) \\
&= (X - 2m \times \pi) - 2m \times \epsilon
\end{aligned}
$$

So the *Reduced.X* calculated consists of the true reduced argument plus the error term $-2m \times \epsilon$. As m is $INT(\frac{X}{2\pi})$ this error grows unacceptably large as X grows — for example at $X = 100\pi$ the error will be 6 bits. To get around this problem an approximation to this error can be added back to the remainder by multiplying an approximation of ϵ by $INT(\frac{X}{2\pi})$. In effect this is using a value of π with twice as many significant bits as the format provides.

This error correction is needed in all the standard functions so support for it is useful. When calculating a remainder the quotient is also being developed so the remainder instruction returns the quotient in **FBreg** under certain conditions. If X is very much larger than Y then $INT(\frac{X}{Y})$ cannot be exactly represented in the floating point format. Sufficient conditions for **FBreg** to contain the quotient after the remainder are that $(X.exp - Y.exp)$ is less than 20 for single length and 30 for double length values. If this is the case then a fast and accurate range reduction of X into $[-\frac{1}{2}Y, \frac{1}{2}Y]$ can be implemented by

```
(load X); (load Y); (remainder instruction sequence); fprev;
(load Y.error); fpmul; fpadd; (load Y); fpremfirst
```

The *fpremfirst* at the end is required because after adding the error term the result may possibly lie just outside the range $[-\frac{1}{2}Y, \frac{1}{2}Y]$. If Y has last bit accuracy then this can be corrected by taking the remainder of this corrected remainder by Y. Since the erroneous result will be only just outside the required range then the remainder will only execute the *fpremfirst* instruction before jumping out of the sequence, hence only that instruction is required.

7.5.6   Loading and multiplying by special values

fpldzerosn	load single length 0.0
fpldzerodb	load double length 0.0
fpumulby2	multiply by 2.0
fpudivby2	divide by 2.0
fpuexpinc32	multiply by 2^{32}
fpuexpdec32	divide by 2^{32}

Loading constants into the floating point unit involves forming a pointer into a table of constants and transferring the data from memory into the floating point register. Since 0.0 is a fairly common constant, two instructions *fpldzerosn* and *fpldzerodb* are provided to load 0.0 immediately.

Also multiplication and division by 2.0 is fairly common. Two instructions *fpumulby2* and *fpudivby2* perform this with correct handling of overflows and underflows according to the IEEE standard. These are considerably faster than loading 2.0 and doing an *fpmul* or *fpdiv* as they operate directly on the exponent of the value in **FAreg**.

Similarily multiplication and division by 2^{32} are provided by *fpuexpinc32* and *fpuexpdec32* mainly for use in the conversion routines. These also handle overflows and underflows according to the IEEE standard.

7.5.7   Sign bit manipulation

fpuabs   floating point absolute value

fpuabs replaces **FAreg** with its absolute value. i.e. it makes the sign bit positive — n.b. the sign bit of Not-a-Numbers may be changed even though they do not have a 'numeric' value and the IEEE standard does not define what the sign bit of a Not-a-Numbers signifies. *fpuabs* will set the floating point error flag if the value in **FAreg** is an infinity or a Not-a-Number.

7.5.8   Load and operate instructions

fpldnladdsn	load and add single length floating point number
fpldnladddb	load and add double length floating point number
fpldnlmulsn	load and multiply single length floating point number
fpldnlmuldb	load and multiply double length floating point number

To make the floating point code more compact some common pairs of instructions can be replaced with a single instruction. These are the four instructions with the greatest effect on the size of code.

fpldnladdsn	=	*fpldnlsn; fpadd*
fpldnladddb	=	*fpldnldb; fpadd*
fpldnlmulsn	=	*fpldnlsn; fpmul*
fpldnlmuldb	=	*fpldnldb; fpmul*

7.6   Comparisons

fpgt	floating point greater than
fpeq	floating point equality
fpordered	floating point orderability

Three instructions are provided as primitives for building comparison operations. All the multitude of comparisions given in the IEEE standard can be constructed from these instructions. *fpgt* and *fpeq* both perform *(FBreg comp FAreg)*. *fpordered* tests if **FAreg** and **FBreg** can be ordered in the IEEE sense where Not-a-Numbers are considered to be noncomparable with any floating point number — including themselves.

fpgt and *fpeq* pop **FAreg** and **FBreg** off the floating point stack and set the floating point error flag if either is a Not-a-Number or an infinity. *fpordered* does not alter the floating point registers. All three operations return their result as a boolean value in **Areg**.

7.6.1   Ordinary magnitude comparison

These are provided by using *fpgt* and *fpeq* to generate the required comparisons. In this case Not-a-Numbers and Infs are considered as normal floating point numbers with a maximum exponent. Comparison of finite numbers with Not-a-Numbers here can cause unexpected results as in arithmetic the sign of Not-a-Numbers has no meaning while here the sign is important.

7.6.2   IEEE magnitude comparison

The IEEE standard lays down that — in general — Not-a-Numbers are not comparable with anything. i.e. X *comp* Y is always false if either X or Y is a Not-a-Number. These comparisons are somewhat safer than magnitude comparison if there is the possibility of Not-a-Numbers being created in a program but has the disadvantage that implications such as

$$\neg(X < Y) \Rightarrow X \geq Y$$

no longer hold.

The IEEE comparisons can be implemented using the following three primitives

Unordered

>   *fpordered; eqc 0*

IEEE greater than

>   *fpordered; fpgt; and*

IEEE equality

>   *fpordered; fpeq; and*

7.7   Class analysis

>   *fpnan*   test for Not-a-Number
>   *fpnotfinite*   test for Not-a-Number or infinity

These two instructions are provided to allow a rudimentary check to be made on the class of the value held in **FAreg**. Both return a boolean value in **Areg** and do not affect the floating point stack.

fpnan tests to see if **FAreg** is a Not-a-Number and *fpnotfinite* tests to see if **FAreg** is not finite — i.e. is a Not-a-Number or an infinity.

7.8   Floating point error handling

The errors that can occur can be first split into two broad categories — floating point errors and non floating point errors. Non floating point errors are the same types of error that occur on the IMS T414 — range violation on array access, failure of all conditionals on an **IF** statement, checked integer arithmetic overflow, etc. Floating point errors are due to a bad evaluation being performed in the floating point unit. Examples of this are evaluations that overflow the real range, evaluations that have no meaning (e.g. 0/0) and division by zero. The IEEE 754 standard is designed to be as robust as possible in that it will give as good a result as possible in these cases by possibly using an 'infinity' or a 'Not-a-Number' as an error flag. With these methods evaluation of an expression can continue with the effects of the bad sub-evaluation slowly spreading through the terms. This way the IEEE standard enables a result to be returned in all cases. Evaluations in which one of the errors has been 'corrected' must be signalled as the result will not be the infinitely precise result correctly rounded. For example if X and Y are both finite and positive and $X + Y$ overflows then $(X + Y) - Y$ will be an infinity rather than X as might be expected.

Non floating point errors are considered to be of a much greater severity than floating point errors. Floating point errors are often due to 'bad' data being used in an evaluation. The non floating point errors are, in general, caused by more than just bad data — an array index may be being incorrectly formed, all the conditionals of an **IF** statement have failed or an incorrect assumption on the range of a variable has caused an overflow. In addition, unlike the floating point standard, there is no provision for returning the 'best' result possible under these circumstances. The cause of a floating point error is often only 'bad' input values to an algorithm whereas a non floating point error is probably caused by a bug in the algorithm itself.

To cope with these two varieties of error there are two error flags on the IMS T800. There is the error flag as on the IMS T414. This is set by all non floating point errors and the processor can be made to halt if it becomes set. In addition there is an error flag on the floating point unit to show whether a floating point error has occurred. This flag can be OR-ed into the main error flag if the user wants to treat floating point errors at the same level as other errors — for instance in a safety critical control module.

7.8.1   Non floating point error handling

This is the same as on the IMS T414. All the errors that are flagged on the IMS T414 are also flagged on the IMS T800.

7.8.2   Floating point error handling

The floating point error flag of IMS T800 can be used to partially implement the IEEE 754 exceptions. The IEEE standard is not fully implemented for two main reasons. Firstly the amount of extra complexity needed to implement exceptions fully — needing to have access to 5 additional flags etc — did not appear justified by their usefulness. Secondly it is extremely difficult to embed the ideas of exceptions in a language. This applies especially to a language like occam which benefits from precise algebraic semantics. Because of this it has been decided to not implement IEEE exceptions in hardware. Instead the standard occam mechanism of causing erroneous procedures to **STOP** are used. Software can be written to provide the full IEEE exception flags although performance will be decreased.

The various floating point errors will now be dealt with individually.

Invalid operation

The IEEE standard defines arithmetic in terms of rounding infinitely precise results. Infinite arguments are handled by taking the limit of the operation when the infinity is replaced by arbitrarily large values of the correct sign. However under this scheme there are some operations that have no meaning. These are

Not-a-Number Arithmetic Not-a-Numbers have no value — so arithmetic cannot be performed on them

Infinity addition *(+infinity) + (−infinity)* has no meaning using limits

0 × infinity

bad division *0/0* and *infinity/infinity* have no meaning

bad remainder *x REM y* has no meaning if *y* is 0 or *x* is infinite

negative square root square root of a negative number has no meaning

The case of *0 × infinity* is slightly different from the others as, using limits, the result 0 can be obtained. However, since the 0 could be due to an underflow and the infinity due to an overflow, giving any 'numeric' result could be misleading so a 'Not-a-Number' is returned.

Not-a-Number Arithmetic

If only one argument is a Not-a-Number then it is returned as the result so that error messages are propagated through expressions. If both arguments are Not-a-Numbers then to meet the IEEE standard one must be returned — in the IMS T800 the choice has been made to return the Not-a-Number with the larger fractional part.

All the other cases return a (different) Not-a-Number. In this way if the result of an operation is a Not-a-Number it is possible to detect what type of error has occurred. This is more than is required by IEEE 754.

Division by zero

If a finite non-zero number is divided by zero then the error flag is set and a correctly signed infinity is returned. The error flag is set even though infinity is the 'correct' answer due to the over-loading of infinity that is described later. In many cases this error probably signifies some earlier underflow error.

Overflow

If, when the infinitely precise result is rounded keeping the exponent range unbounded, the value lies outside the bounds of the floating point format then an overflow error has occurred. The IEEE 754 standard lays down what result to return in these cases, either infinity or the largest finite number in the standard depending on rounding mode, and the IMS T800 conforms to this. The error flag is set to signify that the result is not the correctly rounded result but the best result available in the format.

Infinity

The previous two sections have described how infinities can be produced — either through division by zero or by overflows. These two methods, however, do not produce the same actual result — in the case of division by zero the answer is a true infinity while with overflow the infinity result is only signifying that the true answer is finite but outside the range of the format. If arithmetic is done to infinite precision then these two quantities behave in radically different ways. For this reason on the IMS T800 all arithmetic involving an infinite argument will set the error flag. If a true infinity is being used as an argument then the error flag probably ought to signal the presence of infinity. If an overflow infinity is being used then the error flag is set to warn that the evaluation may differ substantially from that obtained from using infinitely precise arithmetic throughout.

Underflow and inexact

These are exceptions in the IEEE 754 standard but are not implemented in the IMS T800.

7.8.3   Error handling instructions

fpchkerr	check floating point error
fptesterr	test and clear floating point error
fpuseterr	set floating point error
fpuclrerr	clear floating point error

The floating point error flag is the means by which the IMS T800 implements an error detection scheme similar to the exceptions of the IEEE 754 standard. There are four operations that allow the floating point error flag to be manipulated directly. *fpuseterr* and *fpuclrerr* directly set and clear the flag. *fptesterr* sets **Areg** to *true* if the floating point error flag was clear and to *false* otherwise. *fptesterr* also clears the floating point error flag. The final instruction, *fpchkerr*, is intended to support checked arithmetic as it ORs the floating point error flag into the main error flag. Using *fpchkerr*, the presence of errors in floating point arithmetic can be given equal importance to errors on the main processor caused by integer overflows or program faults such as range violation.

In arithmetic the floating point error flag is set in circumstances in which the invalid operation, division by zero or overflow exceptions would be flagged. In addition the flag is set if an input to a floating point operation is infinite — this is due to the fact that since infinities are either true infinities or merely overflows a warning that an infinity is being used seems helpful.

The earlier section on expressions described how the code to evaluate floating point expressions could be constructed in almost the same way as for integer expressions. This made no reference to error checking. If the language supports only totally unchecked or totally checked floating point arithmetic then this method will still work and the next two paragraphs explain how to achieve this. If expressions are allowed to contain both checked and unchecked arithmetic then a more complex mechanism is required which is detailed in a later section.

7.8.4   Unchecked arithmetic

In the simplest scheme in which all floating point arithmetic is done without error checking — i.e. relying on the IEEE representation to cope with 'errors' — the code to evaluate expressions will make no reference to the floating point error flag. This way any errors that occur are only flagged in the floating point error flag which has no effect on the execution of the program.

7.8.5   Checked arithmetic

The next scheme is fully checked with error checking performed for each assignment. In this scheme an entire expression is evaluated before checking to see if an error has occurred in the evaluation. The code to evaluate the expression *exp* in this way is

> *fpuclrerr; exp; fpchkerr*

This clears the floating point error flag, evaluates the expression and then ORs the floating point error flag into the main error flag. So, if there is a floating point error in the expression, the error flag is set afterwards.

It is important that there is no possibility of the process being timesliced or descheduled during the evaluation of *exp* as the value of the floating point error flag is not preserved over descheduling.

It is not sufficient for error checking to check the result of an expression to see if it is an infinity or a Not-a-Number to decide if an error has occurred. This is because it is possible to cause an overflow error producing an infinity and then divide some finite number by that infinity which will produce a zero result. Instead the floating point error flag must be used.

7.9   Type conversion

The floating point unit has facilities to enable conversions between the integer types and the floating point types **REAL32** and **REAL64**. Several instructions are provided to perform the component parts of the various conversions. Each conversion can be constructed by using a suitable sequence of these components.

7.9.1   REAL to REAL conversions

> *fpur32tor64*   convert from single length to double length
> *fpur64tor32*   convert from double length to single length

The two instructions *fpur32tor64* and *fpur64tor32* convert the floating point value in **FAreg** from one floating point format to the other. *fpur32tor64* is an exact conversion involving no rounding. *fpur64tor32* rounds during the conversion so a set rounding mode operation must precede it if a rounding mode other than *Round-to-Nearest* is required.

An infinity is represented in the IEEE standard by a floating point number with maximum exponent but zero fraction. A Not-a-Number has a maximum exponent but a non-zero fraction. When converting from one format to the other infinities are preserved. When a Not-a-Number is converted from **REAL32** to **REAL64** the old fractional part is padded with zeros to the right. If a Not-a-Number is converted from **REAL64** to **REAL32** by truncating the fractional part could leave the fraction as zero — i.e. causing it to be infinity. So instead all **REAL64** Not-a-Numbers are converted into a special Not-a-Number — the *Real64toReal32conversionNaN*. In this way a **REAL64** Not-a-Number cannot become a **REAL32** infinity by truncating its fraction.

7.9.2   REAL to INT conversions

> *fpint*   round to 'floating integer'
> *fpstnli32*   store 'floating integer' as integer
> *fpuchki32*   check in **INT32** range
> *fpuchki64*   check in **INT64** range
> *fprtoi32*   round and check to **INT32** range

fpint converts a floating point number to an integer value in the floating point format. This is the *'Round Floating-Point Number to Integer Value'* function specified by the IEEE standard. It takes the value in **FAreg** and rounds it, according to the rounding mode, to an integer value. If a rounding mode other than *Round-to-Nearest* is required for the conversion then this instruction should be preceded immediately by the mode selection instruction. For example if **FAreg** contained *345.231* then after

> *fpurp; fpint*

FAreg would contain *346.0*.

fpstnli32 truncates the value in **FAreg** to an integer value and stores the bottom 32 bits of that integer representation into the address pointed to by **Areg**. The truncation is performed to allow the same instruction to be used to store the two 32 bit halves of an **INT64**. Rounding to an integer must first be performed by *fpint*.

fpuchki32 and *fpuchki64* check that the contents of **FAreg** (regardless of type) lie in the range of the relevant integer type. This assumes that **FAreg** has already been rounded to an integer value by a preceding *fpint* instruction. If the value lies outside the range then the floating point error flag is set. If a conversion is to be error checked then this instruction should be followed by an *fpchkerr* instruction — and possibly preceded by *fpuclrerr* to isolate any error to this instruction.

Code sequences for the conversions to integer from real are

REAL to **INT32** *Round-to-Nearest* mode, error checked, storing the result in X

>   *fpint; fpuclrerr; fpuchki32; fpchkerr; X; fpstnli32*

REAL to **INT64** truncated (*Round-to-Zero* mode), unchecked, storing the result in Y

>   *fpurz; fpint; Y; fpdup; dup; fpstnli32; ldnlp 1; fpuexpdec32; fpstnli32*

To aid code compactness the most common **REAL** to **INT32** case

>   *fpint; fpuchki32*

can be replaced with the single instruction

>   *fprtoi32*

7.9.3   INT to REAL conversions

fpi32tor32	load **INT32** as single length floating point number
fpi32tor64	load **INT32** as double length floating point number
fpb32tor64	load unsigned 32 bit integer as double length floating point number
fpunoround	convert from double length to single length without rounding

fpi32tor32 takes the **INT32** value from the address contained in **Areg** and rounds this to a single length floating point number of the same value in **FAreg**. This should be preceded by a round mode selection instruction if a rounding mode other than *Round-to-Nearest* is required.

fpi32tor64 takes the **INT32** value from the address contained in **Areg** and converts this to a double length floating point number of the same value in **FAreg**. This is an exact conversion.

fpb32tor64 takes the unsigned 32 bit value from the address contained in **Areg** and converts this to a double length floating point number of the same value in **FAreg**. This is an exact conversion. It is used to load the bottom word of an **INT64** during its conversion to a floating point representation.

fpunoround does a **REAL64** to **REAL32** conversion which does not round the mantissa. This instruction only works for normal numbers and zeros. It is used to remove the introduction of double rounding errors when **INT64**s are converted into **REAL32**s. This instruction is not intended for use outside these code sequences.

The various conversions can be provided by the following code sequences. Each sequence should be preceded by code to load the address of the value to be converted into **Areg** and followed by code to store the converted value into its destination if necessary. Where necessary the rounding mode for the conversion can be set.

INT32 to **REAL32** in *Round-to-Zero* mode

>   *fpurz; fpi32tor32*

INT32 to **REAL64** in *Round-to-Nearest* mode

>   *fpi32tor64*

INT64 to **REAL64** in *Round-to-Nearest* mode

>   *dup; fpb32tor64; ldnlp 1; fpi32tor64; fpuexpinc32; fpadd*

INT64 to **REAL32** in *Round-to-Minus-Infinity* mode

>   *dup; fpb32tor64; fpunoround; ldnlp 1; fpi32tor64; fpuexpinc32; fpunoround; fpurm; fpadd*

In the conversions from **INT64** the round mode selection takes place immediately before the results from converting the two halves of the **INT64** are added together as the sub-conversions from integer to **REAL** are exact.

7.10   Saving the floating point unit state

In the same manner that information must not be left on the main processor stack when a process may be descheduled care must be taken with the floating point stack.

7.10.1   Timeslicing and descheduling

The floating point registers are not saved when a process is descheduled. This is the same as for the integer registers. To take account of this a compiler must ensure that at points where descheduling may occur — *j*, *lend*, channel communication, timer input or alternative wait — there is no information being stored on the floating point stack. Any data that is needed later must be stored in temporary variables.

When a process is scheduled it can make no assumptions about the contents of the floating point registers. If the floating point unit is to be used then data will need to be loaded into the floating point registers thus setting the round mode to *Round-to-Nearest*. Hence the value of the rounding mode when a process is scheduled, and by implication when a process is descheduled, is irrelevant.

The value held in the floating point error flag when one process is descheduled can, though, affect the next process. For this reason all floating point error checking should be limited to portions of code that cannot be descheduled. As floating point error checking can usually be performed over the evaluation of individual expressions this should cause no limitations.

7.10.2   Interrupts

When a high priority process interrupts a low priority process the floating point unit state is copied into save registers and retrieved when control is returned to the low priority process. These save registers are in the floating point unit and the entire state can be pushed into them at the same time. Because of this the need to save the floating point state increases the maximum interrupt latency only by a small amount. A high priority process will only relinquish control when it terminates or needs to wait for a communication. The conditions required to ensure correct behaviour of low priority processes are sufficient to ensure correct behaviour of high priority processes.

Because of the concurrent operation of two processing units in the IMS T800 the exact description of what happens on an interrupt is slightly more complex than for a non floating point transputer. When a high priority process interrupts a low priority process each processing unit will be interrupted as soon as it ends the instruction it was executing, or in the case of an interruptable instruction such as *move* it reaches the

integer unit		floating point unit	time	
. . .		. . .	0	
fpdiv	→	start division	2	
fpdiv	fpu busy	calculating	4	**INTERRUPT**
	fpu busy	finished	34	
interrupted	→	start division	35	
saving registers	fpu busy	calculating		
	fpu busy	finished	67	
		interrupted	68	
push fpu state	→	push fpu state	69	

Figure 7.3 Interrupting the floating point unit

next interrupt point. Then the integer processor can start to handle the interrupt even if the floating point unit is still executing a floating point operation. The integer processor will save various registers into the register save area and then synchronize with the floating point unit to copy its registers into the saved set. If the low priority process was not using floating point arithmetic then the maximum interrupt latency will be almost the same as for the IMS T414. If the low priority process was making use of the floating point unit then the maximum interrupt latency will be slightly longer.

To demonstrate how interrupts are handled consider the program shown in figure 7.3. This is an example in which the interrupt takes an unusually long time to be handled.

In this example the high priority process will not execute until around 70 cycles after the interrupt occurred as two floating point divisions had to be completed on the fpu. In general interrupt response will be markedly better than this.

The worst case interrupt latency for the IMS T800-20 is around 75 cycles (3.5μs) when the floating point unit is being used. In applications where the floating point unit is unused it remains at around 50 cycles (2.5μs) as for the IMS T414-20.

More information on the synchronisation between the main processor and the floating point unit is given in a later chapter.

7.11   Floating point support for IMS T414

The following instructions are included to support single length (32 bit) IEEE 754 real arithmetic on 32 bit transputers without a floating point unit. By moving some of the work that is performed in all floating point operations into micro-code the performance of floating point arithmetic is almost doubled.

unpacksn	unpack single length fp number
roundsn	round single length fp number
postnormsn	post-normalise single length fp number
ldinf	load single length infinity
cflerr	check single length infinity or Not-a-Number

7.11.1   Unpacking a floating point number

unpacksn takes a packed IEEE single length floating point number in **Areg**. It then returns the exponent in **Breg** and the fractional field in **Areg** — this will not include the implied most significant bit for normalised numbers. In addition a value indicating the type of number is added to 4 times the initial value of **Breg** and left in **Creg**. The values added are

0   if **Areg** is zero
1   if **Areg** is a denormalised or normalised number
2   if **Areg** is an infinity
3   if **Areg** is a Not-a-Number

The following sequence can be used to unpack the operands to *X op Y*

> *ldl op; ldl X; unpacksn; stl Xfrac; stl Xexp; ldl Y; unpacksn; stl Yfrac; stl Yexp*

where the value left in **Areg** codes the operation and the types of the operands. This value can then be used to access a table of addresses of the code sequences to evaluate each operation/operand type combination.

7.11.2   Packing a floating point number

roundsn and *postnormsn* along with *norm* can be used to normalise, round and pack the result of a floating point operation. If an operation has been performed resulting in a sign bit in *sign*, an exponent in *exp* and an unnormalised fraction in *frac* and *guard* then the following instruction sequence will pack the result into **Areg**. Overflowing and denormalised results are handled correctly and rounding is performed in *Round-to-Nearest* mode as defined in IEEE 754.

> *ldl exp; stl 0; ldl frac; ldl guard; norm; postnormsn; roundsn; ldl sign; or*

Note that this makes use of (**Wptr**+0) .

7.11.3   Infinity and Not-a-Numbers

ldinf loads the single length floating point number +infinity onto the register stack.

cflerr sets the error flag if the value in **Areg** is an infinity or a Not-a-Number.

7.12   Implementing floating point arithmetic

INMOS has an implementation of real arithmetic that evaluates arithmetic results in compliance to the IEEE 754 floating point arithmetic standard. This compliance has been verified by formal proof techniques. Library procedures to evaluate standard functions have also been implemented. These will be made available and INMOS strongly recommends that implementors use these rather than writing their own versions as the effort required to correctly implement such procedures is quite large.

8 Specialist instructions

8.1 Two dimensional block move

Graphical applications often require the movement of 2 dimensional blocks of data to perform windowing, overlaying etc. The IMS T800 contains instructions to perform efficient copying, overlaying and clipping of graphics pictures based on byte sized pixels.

move2dinit	initialise 2 dimensional block move
move2dall	2 dimensional block copy
move2dnonzero	2 dimensional block copy non zero bytes
move2dzero	2 dimensional block copy zero bytes

To perform a 2 dimensional move 6 parameters are required. These are

- The address of first element of the source of the copy.

- The address of first element of the destination of the copy.

- The width in bytes of each row to be copied.

- The length or number of rows to be copied.

- The stride of the source array.

- The stride of the destination array.

The stride of an array is the number of bytes in a row. The two stride values are needed to allow a block to be copied from part of one array to another array where the arrays can be of differing size.

The *move2dinit* instruction sets up 3 of these parameters. It takes the *source stride* in **Creg**, the *destination stride* in **Breg** and the *length* in **Areg**. This must be performed before every 2 dimensional block move.

Each of the 3 move instructions has the *source address* in **Creg**, the *destination address* in **Breg** and the *width* in **Areg**.

move2dall copies the whole of the block of *length* rows each of *width* bytes from the source to the destination.

move2dnonzero copies the non zero bytes in the block leaving the bytes in the destination corresponding to the zero bytes in the source unchanged. This can be used to overlay a non rectangular picture onto another picture.

move2dzero copies the zero bytes in the block leaving the bytes in the destination corresponding to the non zero bytes in the source unchanged. This can be used to mask out a non rectangular shape from a picture.

None of the 2 dimensional moves has any affect if either the *width* or *length* of the block to copy is equal to zero. They are all undefined if either the width or length is negative. Also a 2 dimensional block move only makes sense if the *source stride* and *destination stride* are both greater or equal to the *width* of the block being moved. The effect of the 2 dimensional moves is undefined if the source and destination blocks overlap.

8.1.1   Two dimensional block move on other transputers

The original *move* instruction can be used in a loop to perform 2 dimensional block moves on transputers without these additional instructions. The following code sequence performs the *move2dall* function.

```
           ldc 0; stl x; length; stl x+1;
           ldl x+1; cj end;
           source; stl x+2; source.stride; stl x+3;
           dest; stl x+4; dest.stride; stl x+5;
           width; stl x+6;
    L:     ldl x+2; ldl x+4; ldl x+6; move;
           ldl x+2; ldl x+3; sum; stl x+2;
           ldl x+4; ldl x+5; sum; stl x+4;
           ldlp x; ldc (END−L); lend;
    END:
```

8.2   Bit manipulation and CRC evaluation

Instructions have been added to the IMS T800 to allow some of the low level bit manipulation required in implementing communication protocols etc. to be performed efficiently.

> *bitcnt*   count number of bits set in word

bitcnt counts the number of bits that are set in **Areg** and adds this onto an accumulating total held in **Breg** returning the result in **Areg**. **Creg** is popped up into **Breg**. The use of a register to accumulate the total number of bits set means that this instruction can be used in an inline sequence or a loop controlled by a conditional jump to count bits set in an array of words efficiently. Note that a loop using *lend* cannot be used as this has the potential of timeslicing. The instruction takes time proportional to the position of the most significant bit set in the word. This instruction has applications in pattern matching and image recognition.

> *bitrevword*   reverse bits in a word
> *bitrevnbits*   reverse bottom n bits
> *crcword*   perform cyclic redundancy check on a word
> *crcbyte*   perform cyclic redundancy check on a byte

bitrevword reverses the bit pattern of the word held in **Areg**. **Breg** and **Creg** are left unchanged. *bitrevnbits* reverses the bottom **Areg** bits in **Breg**, zeroing all more significant bits, leaving the result in **Areg** and popping **Creg** up into **Breg**. Like the shift instructions this result is undefined if **Areg** is greater than the wordlength and the instruction will take time proportional to **Areg** to execute.

These instructions are useful when interfacing the 'little-endian' transputer with other systems that are 'big-endian'.

crcword and *crcbyte* are component instructions in the calculation of the cyclic redundancy check word for a message. This method for checking the correctness of data that has been communicated is based on polynomial division. Both instructions take the data to be processed in **Areg** – though for *crcbyte* it must be in the most significant byte of the word. **Breg** contains the CRC that has already been generated and **Creg** contains the generator. The CRC is calculated by iterating a loop for *bitsperword* or *bitsperbyte* iterations. The CRC for one bit is performed by shifting **Breg** and **Areg** left one place as a double word quantity (most significant word in **Breg**) then xor-ing **Creg** into the resulting **Breg** if the bit shifted out of **Breg** was set to 1. At the end the new CRC word generated in **Breg** is left in **Areg** and the generator is left in **Breg**.

8.2.1   Calculating the CRC of a message

The *crcword* and *crcbyte* instructions are designed to be used sequentially in in-line code to enable efficient generation of the CRC of a message.

If a message is word aligned then the CRC can be calculated by loading the generator and the first word of the message onto the stack. Then each remaining word in turn is loaded and *crcword* applied to it.

The CRC generation can be coded into a loop using *lend*. **Areg** and **Breg** must be preserved over the *lend* instruction in two locals as the process could be timesliced. The following code would evaluate the CRC of a word aligned message *mess* of *len* words.

```
        ldc 0; stl i; ldl len; stl i+1;
        ldc generator; ldc 0; stl temp1; stl temp2;
L:      ldl temp2; ldl i; ldl message; wsub; ldnl 0; ldl temp1; rev;
        crcword; stl temp1; stl temp2; ldlp i; ldc (END−L); lend;
END:
```

If the message is not word aligned then more care is needed. *crcbyte* is used to handle any nonword aligned bytes at either end of the message.

The overhead involved in handling the loop can be reduced by putting more than one *crcword* in-line inside the loop body.

Remember that the transputer is totally 'little-endian' in that more significant data is always to the left of less significant data or at a more positive address. This applies to bits in bytes, bytes in words and words in arrays.

Communications protocols and standard CRCs differ widely in the way they order data so that to calculate the CRC of a message it will often be necessary to use the *bitrevword* and *bitrevnbits* instructions to handle this. Care is needed to ensure that the CRC being calculated is the same as that required and that data is communicated in the correct order. Many protocols make claims of being 'little-endian' or 'big-endian' but this is not always totally correct — for example the CRC is sometimes in the opposite orientation to the data.

8.3   Resetting a channel

In the occam model of processes a channel is the means by which two processes synchronise and communicate. Once a process attempts to communicate on a channel it must wait until the process at the other end is ready to participate in the communication. All channels are assumed to be totally reliable with no possibility of data loss or corruption. This definition allows communication to be easily included inside a programming language — there is no need to have buffering as all communication is synchronised and all the low level message passing protocols are handled by the transputer hardware. More detailed information on the implementation of channel communication in transputers is given later.

However, there may be situations where a less strict definition of communication is needed. A system with several semi-autonomous units can be designed to tolerate the failure of one component. In the strict occam definition, as soon as any unit needs to communicate with the failed unit it will also fail as its communication will never take place and complete. Also, it may be useful to be able to cope with a temporary break in their connection — for example when someone pulls out the wrong cable. In the strict occam model if a break in communication occurred then at least one of the two processes at the ends of the channel would be left waiting to finish the communication. This would probably cause the whole system to deadlock as more and more processes became dependent on the failed communication.

  resetch   reset channel

The *resetch* instruction allows a channel to be reset into its quiescent (non-communicating) state. **Areg** initially contains the address of the channel to be reset. If the channel is a link channel then that link hardware is reset. The channel process word is reset to *NotProcess.p* and its previous value is returned in **Areg**. From the value returned in **Areg** the state of the channel when it was reset can be deduced — if it is *NotProcess.p* then any communication on the channel had finished correctly, while if it is not then **Areg** contains the process descriptor of the channel waiting to communicate. This process id can be used by a *run* instruction to restart the process that is waiting on the reset channel.

WARNING:

resetch is a very low level instruction and must be used with great care. Whenever *resetch* is used the processes that communicate along the channel that is reset must be designed in a way that copes with the channel being reset. *resetch* should never be used as an 'independent' instruction but only as a component of a higher level communication scheme. It should only be used where all other mechanisms — such as timer *ALT*s, sacrificial buffer processes etc. — are insufficient.

INMOS technical note 1 — *Extraordinary use of transputer links* — gives details on mechanisms using *resetch* that provide 'communicate or fail' processes inside occam.

8.3.1   Differences in resetting soft channels and link channels

In the occam model soft and link channels are indistinguishable. This even holds at the transputer instruction set level where the same instructions are used for communication on either type of channel. However, in the unlikely event of a channel error there is a slight difference. Once both ends of a soft channel are ready to communicate then that communication will occur and must complete as it is performed by copying a block of memory. If both ends of a link channel are ready to communicate then the communication will commence but if the link fails during the communication then at least one end of the communication will fail to complete.

Input with timeout

Suppose a process P acts as a data store for various other processes Q_i. If there is a failure in the communication between P and Q_n then it would be unfortunate if this caused the whole system to stop. For instance an operating system ought not to stop if one of the jobs it is running unexpectedly crashes or if someone disconnects a terminal line. One solution to this is to provide a means for abandoning a communication after a certain period of time has elapsed.

An *ALT* construct can be used to detect a communication that does not start in a certain time interval — but, once a communication has been initiated, then the *ALT* would be committed to that communication and this does not handle the situation where the break occurs during the transfer of the message. This problem will not occur with an internal channel as once a communication has started it is guaranteed to finish. For external link channels a failure in communication can occur during the transfer causing an 'unclean' failure where at least one of the processes will not complete its communication.

If it is only necessary to insulate a process from the failure of another process then the use of a buffer process is often sufficient as the communication between the process and buffer process will always fail 'cleanly'.

If, however, it is also necessary to restart the communication — perhaps when the link connection has been mended — then the ability to reset the channel is required. This can be performed by using *resetch*.

```
            Process 1 – this must start to execute first

            SEQ
                dubious.channel ? message
                completed ! 0

            Process 2

            INT ANY :
            ALT
                TIME ? AFTER timeout
                    INT pid :
                    SEQ
                        resetch (dubious.channel, pid)
                        IF
                            pid = NotProcess.p
                                SKIP
                            TRUE
                                run (pid)
                        completed ? ANY
                        ok := FALSE
                completed ? ANY
                    ok := TRUE
```

Figure 8.1 Code to timeout an input

Timing out an external channel

An input along a channel that will time out after a specific time can be implemented by running the two processes shown in figure 8.1 in parallel to completion. The first process must be scheduled in front of the second — i.e. it must start to execute first. The locally declared channel *completed* is used to synchronise their completion

The two processes together attempt to communicate *message* along *dubious.channel* with the provision that the communication is deemed to have failed if it has not completed before time *timeout*. *ok* returns a flag stating whether or not the timeout occurred.

The sequence of events that happen when this is executed are

1. The first process of the *PAR* initiates the communication along *dubious.channel*.

2. The second process waits on the *ALT* until either the communication on *dubious.channel* has finished and the signal along *completed* is received or the timeout occurs.

3. If the *completed* signal is received then the communication along *dubious.channel* succeeded so *ok* is set to *TRUE*.

   If the timeout occurs then the channel is reset. There are now two cases to consider.

   (a) Between the timeout being selected and the channel being reset the communication on *dubious.channel* has completed — here the *resetch* has had no effect and the signal on *completed* needs to be received.

(b) The communication on *dubious.channel* has still not finished. The process id returned from *resetch* must be the id of the first process in the *PAR* so by using the *run* instruction the input can be aborted and the process restarted at *completed ! 0*.

Both these options need the signal along *completed* to be received and *ok* to be set to *FALSE* to show that the timeout was taken.

The important points in this method are

- The process id returned by *resetch* must be checked in case the communication finished between the timeout being selected and the channel being reset.

- Both alternatives must receive the message on *completed*.

- The communication must be initiated along *dubious.channel* before a timeout can be taken as the channel must only be reset after this communication has started.

- The processes must be coded to prevent them from being timesliced — in particular this means they must not use unconditional jumps — *j*.

- Compiling as an occam *PAR* will not guarantee the last two conditions as occam makes no statements about the order of execution of parallel processes or of timeslice behaviour.

If communication is to be reattempted along *dubious.channel* then the process at the other end of the channel needs to have some similar method to detect when its output has failed. The INMOS technical note 1 gives an example of how to implement communicating processes that will tolerate a disconnection and will restart communication when reconnected.

Similar mechanisms

The same method can be used to provide a timed out output, and a simple modification can provide a communication that can be 'killed' by a signal down a control channel. These should only be used in situations were reconnection of a failed channel is required. If insulation from 'unclean' failure only is needed then a buffer process should be used.

9 Bootstrapping and analysing

The information in this chapter is not needed where system configuration is performed using the transputer development system. It describes how a transputer system is initialised and ways in which it can be debugged. This is not intended as a detailed description of booting and analysing transputers.

9.1 Resetting and analysing

A transputer is reset in order to initialise its internal state and external memory interface, and then to boot. If a transputer is active when it is reset it stops operation immediately. A transputer is reset by pulsing the Reset pin whilst holding the Analyse pin low.

A transputer is analysed in order to investigate its internal state. It stops operation in a way that preserves much of its state and then starts to boot; it does not initialise its external memory interface. A transputer is analysed by taking and holding the Analyse pin high, then pulsing the Reset pin and then taking the Analyse pin low.

After a transputer has booted it is possible to tell whether the transputer was reset or analysed by executing the following instruction.

> *testpranal*   test processor analysing

This will push *true* onto the stack if the processor was analysed or *false* if the processor was reset. This is needed for the process that is executed when the transputer is booting from ROM to determine whether it has just been reset or analysed.

9.2 Reset and power up

The following registers and special memory locations are not initialised when the machine powers on or is reset.

ClockReg$_0$	high priority clock register
ClockReg$_1$	low priority clock register
TPtrLoc$_0$	high priority timer list pointer
TPtrLoc$_1$	low priority timer list pointer
TNextReg$_0$	high priority timeout register
TNextReg$_1$	low priority timeout register
FPtrReg$_0$	high priority scheduling list
BPtrReg$_0$	
FPtrReg$_1$	low priority scheduling list
BPtrReg$_1$	
ErrorFlag	
HaltOnErrorFlag	

The floating point unit, if present, is not initialised in any way. In particular this means that the following registers are not initialised.

FloatingPointErrorFlag, **FAreg**, **FBreg** and **FCreg**

9.2.1   Booting

The way in which a transputer boots is controlled by the **BootFromRom** pin. If this pin is held high then the transputer will boot from ROM, if it is held low the transputer will boot from a link.

Booting from ROM

The transputer starts executing in the following state:

Registers	Iptr	=	*ResetCode*	two bytes below the top of memory
	Wdesc	=	*MemStart* **BITOR** 1	low priority, first free word of memory
	Areg	=	previous value of **Iptr**	
	Breg	=	previous value of **Wdesc**	
	Creg		is undefined	

Flags   The **ErrorFlag** and **HaltOnErrorFlag** are preserved.

Clocks The clocks are stopped.

Booting, peeking and poking down links

The transputer waits until it receives a communication along any one of its links. It then interprets the following data on that link according to the value of the first byte.

If the value of the first byte received is 0 then a word of address is input, followed by a word of data which is written to that address. The transputer then returns to its previous state waiting for a communication on any one of its links.

If the value of the first byte received is 1 then a word of address is input, a word of data is read from that address and then output down the corresponding output link. The transputer then returns to its previous state waiting for a communication on any one of its links.

N.B. In both these cases the address received does not need to be a word aligned address, and the peek or poke affects the *bytesperword* bytes from that byte address.

If the value of the first byte received is 2 or greater then the transputer inputs that number of bytes (Codelength) into its memory, starting at *MemStart*, and then starts executing in the following state

Registers	Iptr	=	*MemStart*
	Wdesc	=	ffw **BITOR** 1
			where ffw is the smallest word address $\geq$ *Memstart* + Codelength — i.e. low priority, with workspace pointer at first free word of memory
	Areg	=	previous value of **Iptr**
	Breg	=	previous value of **Wdesc**
	Creg	=	pointer to the link from which transputer booted

Flags   The **ErrorFlag** and **HaltOnErrorFlag** are preserved.

Clocks The clocks are stopped.

Queues The values in the process queue pointer registers and timer queue locations are preserved.

Actions to be performed by the booting program

> *sthf*   store high priority front pointer
> *stlf*   store low priority front pointer
> *sttimer*   store and start timer

The high and low priority front of queue registers must be initialised to *NotProcess.p*. This can be done by the following sequence of transputer instructions

> *mint; sthf; mint; stlf*

This must occur before the booting program attempts to pass any messages or run any processes. Because of the way in which the process queues are implemented on the transputer there is no need to initialise the back pointers.

The timer queue words must be initialised to *NotProcess.p* and the clocks must be started by executing store timer instructions. The timer queue words **TPtrLoc$_0$** and **TPtrLoc$_1$** are locations below *MemStart* at the bottom of memory. The following instructions do this

> *mint; mint; stnl* **TPtrOffset$_0$**; *mint; mint; stnl* **TPtrOffset$_1$**;

Where **TPtrOffset$_0$** and **TPtrOffset$_1$** are 9 and 10 respectively.

This must be done before any attempt is made to wait on the timer. In addition before attempting to use the timer at either priority level the timer must be started by executing

> *ldc start_time; sttimer*

The **ErrorFlag** and **HaltOnErrorFlag** must be initialised by executing

> *testerr; clrhalterr*

or

> *testerr; sethalterr*

clrhalterr and *sethalterr* affect the halt on error flag and are described later.

If the transputer has a floating point unit then *fptesterr* also must be executed to reset the floating point error flag and to ensure that the rounding mode is set to *Round-to-Nearest*.

If the transputer is being reset, rather than being analysed, the bottom 9 words of memory should also be set to *NotProcess.p*. These words correspond to the 8 channels provided by the 4 links and the event channel. If the transputer is being analysed then these words should not be altered as their values may be needed during the analysis.

As the time queue words are immediately above the link channel words they may be initialised at the same time by setting the bottom 11 words to *NotProcess.p*.

> *sthb*   store high priority back pointer
> *stlb*   store low priority back pointer

sthb and *stlb* allow the back pointers of the two priority level process queues to be explicitly set.

Explicit manipulation of the scheduling queues is dangerous. The queues are manipulated both by scheduling instructions and external events such as the completion of a link transfer. If the transputer scheduler needs to access the process queues while they are being manipulated by a process then the behaviour can be unexpected.

9.3   Analyse

The Analyse pin exists in order that the state of a transputer system can be investigated. This is achieved by bringing the system to a halt in such a way that the state of the individual transputers in that system can be examined.

The state of the processes executing on an analysed transputer can be examined. The processes in the active set will be found in the linked lists holding the process queues. The processes waiting on the timers, along with the time they are waiting for, will be found in the linked stack holding the timer queues. Processes waiting for communication can be found by examining the channel control words.

A system is analysed by analysing all the transputers in the system in the following manner.

The Analyse pin is asserted which causes the system to come to a halt after a specifiable time. The Reset pin is then asserted while continuing to assert the Analyse pin, for at least the specified Reset hold time and is then taken low, while still asserting the Analyse pin. The Analyse pin is then de-asserted and the transputer will boot. Note that the earliest time at which the transputer is guaranteed to be able to receive a message remains specified relative to the fall of Reset rather than the fall of Analyse.

Analysing a system brings it to a halt as a result of each transputer in the system coming to a halt. The components of the transputer respond to the assertion of Analyse in the following manner

Processor The processor only responds to Analyse at certain points during its operation. When one of these points is reached the processor halts any process which is executing and then ignores any scheduling requests made by the links or the timer.

If the processor is not executing a process when analyse is asserted the processor responds at once and halts immediately.

If the processor is executing a process when analyse is asserted the processor responds by halting at either the next descheduling point or the next point at which a low priority process could potentially be timesliced (this will be an unconditional 'jump' or a 'loop end' instruction) . Note that it is possible for a high priority process to pre-empt a low priority process after analyse has been asserted, in which case the processor will halt during the execution of the high priority process. The **Iptr** of a processor which has been halted in this manner will point to the byte of memory following the final byte of the instruction which caused the process to be halted. A list of instructions during which a process can halt is included at the end of this section.

Clocks The clock stops when analyse is asserted. Any processes waiting for the timer will either be scheduled or will remain on the queue.

Links The assertion of Analyse has no effect on input links; they continue to operate normally, sending acknowledges and making scheduling requests as appropriate. (Any scheduling requests made after the processor has halted will not succeed) .

The assertion of Analyse causes output links to output at most a few more data packets. They respond correctly to acknowledge packets and will make scheduling requests as appropriate. (Any scheduling requests made after the processor has halted will not succeed) . The number of data packets which a link will output after

Analyse is asserted is no more than the number of bytes in a processor word.

9.3.1   Information available after booting an analysed transputer

saveh   save high priority queue registers
savel   save low priority queue registers

saveh stores the contents of the front and back pointers of the high priority scheduling list in locations (**Areg**+0) and (**Areg**+1) respectively. *savel* similarly stores the equivalent low priority scheduling list pointers.

The information that is available for analysing can be found in the following places.

- The value that **Wdesc** had when the processor halted is available in **Breg**. This will be *(NotProcess.p* BITOR *1)* if the processor was not active.

- The value that was in **Iptr** when the processor halted is available in **Areg**.

- The **ErrorFlag** and **HaltOnErrorFlag** are in the same state as when the processor halted.

- Provided that the process word associated with a link channel was initialised to *NotProcess.p* then if that process word contains a process descriptor then the channel was being used for output, (unconditional) input or alternative input when the processor halted.

- If two processes are communicating and waiting on either end of a link then the message being transferred is held in the outputting transputer. If a process has input a message but has not yet resumed execution then the message is held correctly in the inputting transputer.

- The timer list pointer words may be read so the contents of the timer queues may be determined.

- The front and back pointers of the process queues may be read using the *saveh* and *savel* instructions. Thus the contents of the process queues may be determined.

- The register save area may contain information about an interrupted low priority process.

9.3.2   Instructions where the processor will halt for analysis

A process will only halt for analysis when it reaches a point where the current process could be descheduled by timeslicing or communication. Table 9.1 details the instructions after which the processor may halt for analysis and the state in which the processor halts. In none of the cases will the current process have been descheduled — i.e. it will still be the current process when the transputer is analysed.

9.4   Error detection by hardware

Certain run time errors such as arithmetic overflow and subscript errors are checked by transputer instructions. These all signal the presence of an error by setting the sticky **ErrorFlag**. This may be explicitly set, cleared and tested by instructions.

The **ErrorFlag** is sticky only within a priority level.

j	the jump has been taken
lend	the instruction has updated the count locations and the consequential jump has occurred
endp	the process count has been updated but the process has not been descheduled
stopp	the process has not been descheduled
stoperr	the process has not been descheduled
in	the process descriptor has been left in the channel but the process has not been descheduled
out	the process descriptor has been left in the channel and, if the process has output to a channel from which another process was performing alternative input, then that other process has been scheduled. The current process has not been descheduled
outword	as for *out*
outbyte	as for *out*
tin	the process has been inserted into the timer queue but has not been descheduled
altwt	the value *Waiting.p* has been written into the State location but the process has not been descheduled
talwt	the value *Waiting.p* has been written into the State location, the process has been inserted into the timer queue, if appropriate. The process has not been descheduled

Table 9.1 Instructions at which process may halt for analysis

The state of the **ErrorFlag** is brought out of the transputer via the Error pin.

There is a mode of operation where whenever the **ErrorFlag** changes from a 0 (unset) to a 1 (set) the processor is brought to an immediate halt. This mode is selected via the **HaltOnErrorFlag** which may be explicitly set, cleared and tested by instructions.

clrhalterr	clear the **HaltOnErrorFlag**
sethalterr	set the **HaltOnErrorFlag**
testhalterr	test the **HaltOnErrorFlag**

clrhalterr and *sethalterr* clear and set the **HaltOnErrorFlag** while the *testhalterr* pushes its value into **Areg**.

The definition of halt on error is that the processor will halt on a 0 to 1 transition of the **ErrorFlag**. This ensures that a transputer which has been halted as the result of the **ErrorFlag** being set can be booted and analysed whilst preserving both the **ErrorFlag** and **HaltOnErrorFlag**. If the **ErrorFlag** is cleared with the **HaltOnErrorFlag** remaining set, the transputer will halt when the **ErrorFlag** becomes set.

When the processor halts as a result of the **ErrorFlag** becoming set — i.e. with the **HaltOnErrorFlag** set — the **Iptr** will point to the byte of memory which is two bytes beyond the last byte of the instruction which generated the error. (Note that this is not the same as the state of the **Iptr** of a processor which has been analysed) . The processor does not execute any further instructions, does not respond to any Run or Ready requests from the links nor respond to any Timer requests. The timer continues to tick and the links continue to transfer data.

9.4.1   Instructions which may cause the Error flag to be set

Table 9.2 details the instructions which can cause the **ErrorFlag** to be set.

adc	add constant
csub0	check subscript from 0
ccnt1	check count from 1
seterr	set error
add	add
sub	subtract
mul	multiply
div	divide
rem	remainder
cword	check word
csngl	check single
ladd	long add
lsub	long subtract
ldiv	long divide
fmul	fractional multiply
cflerr	check floating point error — *if present*
fpchkerr	floating point check error — *if present*

Table 9.2 Instructions that can cause an error

9.4.2   Differences between halt-on-error and analyse

The state of the **Iptr** of a process which has 'halted on error' or has been analysed can be determined by examining the **Areg** of the processor when it is booted. However, the relationship between the value of the **Iptr** and the instruction which was being executed when the processor halted is different in these two cases.

Where a processor has been analysed the **Iptr** will point to the byte of memory following the final byte of the instruction which caused the process to be halted.

Where a processor has halted as a result of the **ErrorFlag** becoming set (i.e. with the **HaltOnErrorFlag** set), the **Iptr** will point to the byte of memory which is two bytes beyond the last byte of the instruction which generated the error.

9.5   The register save area

Seven locations near the bottom of the transputer's memory map are used to save the processor registers when a high priority process interrupts a low priority process. The design of the process scheduling and priority system means that at most one process is ever interrupted so only one set of registers ever needs to be stored. The memory locations of this register save area are

WdescIntSaveLoc
IptrIntSaveLoc
AregIntSaveLoc
BregIntSaveLoc
CregIntSaveLoc
STATUSIntSaveLoc
EregIntSaveLoc

The first five of these store the registers containing the processor state — the workspace descriptor of the interrupted process, the pointer to the next instruction to execute, and the contents of the evaluation stack. The status register is saved to maintain the value of the error flag of the interrupted process. **Ereg** is an internal register that is used in block move and needs to be saved as block move is interruptable. The value of **Ereg** saved here should be of no interest to users.

The information stored in these locations can be used to provide a form of processor analysis where a high priority process can be used to examine the state of the low priority processes that are executing. However care must be taken to check the validity of the data in the save area. If no low priority process was executing when the high priority process started then **WdescIntSaveLoc** will contain *NotProcess.p* and the other locations will contain undefined data. If a low priority process was executing then all the locations will contain valid data except **EregIntSaveLoc** which is only valid if a block move was interrupted.

The values in these locations should not be changed. In particular the **IptrIntSaveLoc** and **WdescIntSaveLoc** must not be used as a mechanism for replacing the interrupted process with another process.

9.5.1   Two dimensional block move workspace area

On the IMS T800 a further 10 locations above the register save area are used to contain the workspace needed for the 2 dimensional block move instructions. This consists of 2 sets of 5 locations providing workspace for a block move at each priority level. The values held in these registers at any time should be of no interest to users and must not be altered.

9.5.2   Analysing floating point registers

It is not possible to examine the low priority floating point register set from a high priority process. This is because, for efficiency, the registers are stored in the floating point unit in an auxiliary set of registers rather than being stored in the save area.

10 Architectural details

10.1 Process scheduling queues and timer lists

Previous sections have described how the transputer instruction set supports concurrent processes through the use of process and timer queues. However no information about how these queues were organised was given. This is because for almost all purposes programs should not make any attempt to manipulate these queues. The transputer hardware can at any time start to manipulate the queues without reference to the process being executed. If the queues are being altered, there is the danger that the hardware will find them in an 'invalid' state and hence cause unpredictable behaviour.

Programs should not attempt to alter the process or timer queues explicitly — they should always use the instructions provided.

Information on the representation of these queues is given here to enable programs to analyse the state of the transputer.

10.1.1 Process queues

There are two process queues on the transputer — one for each priority level. Each of these queues is represented as a linked list in the transputer with the workspace address of the processes at the front and back held in the front and back pointers. These pointers are held in registers in the transputer. The values in these registers can be obtained by using the *saveh* and *savel* instructions.

Each process in the queue — apart from the last — contains a pointer to the workspace of the next process in the queue. This pointer is the workspace pointer of the following process and is stored in (**Wptr**−2) . The **Iptr** of the process is held in (**Wptr**−1) . An empty queue is signified by the front pointer having the value *NotProcess.p*. The currently executing process does not appear in the queue.

So to extract the workspace pointer of the nth process in the process queue the following pseudo-occam could be used

```
INT wptr:
SEQ
    wptr := front_pointer
    IF
        wptr = NotProcess.p
            ... empty queue
        TRUE
            SEQ i = 0 FOR n
                SEQ
                    wptr := wptr[−2]
                    IF
                        wptr = back_pointer
                            ... not enough entries
                        TRUE
                            SKIP
    result := wptr
```

Error handling code will need to be added to cope with the cases where the queue is either empty or contains less than *n* items.

Similarily, information about each process in a process queue could be printed by

```
INT wptr:
SEQ
    wptr := front_pointer
    IF
        wptr = NotProcess.p
            print.string('empty queue')
        TRUE
            SEQ
                WHILE wptr <> back_pointer
                    SEQ
                        print.info(wptr)
                        wptr := wptr[-2]
                print.info(wptr)
```

Scheduling and the process queues

When a process is scheduled — by execution of *runp* or *startp*, or by a communication completing — the process is added to the back of the relevant priority process queue.

When a low priority process is descheduled due to timeslicing then the process is added to the back of the low priority process queue.

When the transputer requires a new process to run — because the previous process has either stopped (terminated unsuccessfully), ended (terminated successfully) or is waiting for communication — then the process at the front of the relevant priority process queue is restarted.

Manipulation of the process queues

As has been mentioned earlier the explicit manipulation of the process queues is not advised. This is because the transputer hardware may at any time wish to make use of these queues and if the queue is in an invalid state then the transputer's behaviour is unpredicatable.

The process that initiates a transputer after booting must initialise the values of the queue registers. After this the transputer instructions provided to implement scheduling should be used to run concurrent processes.

Explicit queue manipulation should only be done when the instruction set support for scheduling is insufficient. If it is absolutely necessary to manipulate the process queues explicitly then the following points must be noted.

- The transputer may wish to make use of the process queues at any point

- A process manipulating the queues should not allow another process of the priority of the queue it is manipulating to execute while the queue is being manipulated. This means that a low priority process must not manipulate the high priority queue. A low priority process manipulating the low priority queue must not have the potential to timeslice.

- A process cannot be safely appended to the end of a queue as between reading the queue back pointer and updating it the transputer hardware may have rescheduled a process waiting for communication from an external link channel.

- At all points the process queues must contain valid data — i.e. it must be possible to trace a path through the linked list from the front pointer to the back pointer after every instruction.

10.1.2   Timer lists

Each priority level has a timer list. The timer lists contain information about processes that are waiting until a specific time before being restarted. The timer lists are represented as a linked list of workspaces. The address of the workspace of the head of the timer queue is stored in the timer list pointer location. The linked list is implemented by storing the address of the next workspace in (**Wptr**−4) of a process workspace, with the time associated with that workspace stored in (**Wptr**−5) . This is the time at which the process will become ready — so if a process executes

>   *tin X*

the time *(X+1)* will be entered into (**Wptr**−5) . The end of a timer list is signified by a link address of *NotProcess.p*.

Each list is ordered so that each process in the list is waiting for a time no earlier than that of the process before it and no later than that of the process after it. The time of the first process — the next time that is required — is stored in the relevant timeout register.

The information about the contents of the high priority timer list could be printed by

```
INT wptr:
SEQ
    wptr := timer_list_pointer₀
    WHILE wptr <> NotProcess.p
        SEQ
            print.info(wptr)
            wptr := wptr[−4]
```

Timer input

When a timer input is performed — either because of a *tin* instruction or by a timer guard in an **ALT** statement — then the process is inserted into the relevant timer list. This involves searching down the list until the time requested lies between the times of two adjacent entries so that when the process is inserted there the ordering of the list is maintained. This means that instructions that manipulate the timer lists take time proportional to the length of the timer lists. Because of this, these instructions are interruptable.

Manipulating the timer lists

Similar considerations to those concerned with the manipulation of process queues apply here. In general once the initialising process has initialised the process lists, they should not be modified explicitly. Timer list manipulation is, in fact, more difficult as the validity of the timeout register must be maintained and this register is not accessable.

10.2   Special RAM locations

Mention has been made in various sections of special RAM locations near the bottom of memory. These are reserved RAM locations used as if they were additional registers. Because the transputer has on chip RAM the memory for these registers is guaranteed to be present. In normal use programs will not need to look at the values in these locations but, for instance, when debugging or analysing a transputer their contents are useful.

The special RAM locations, and their uses are shown in table 10.1. The **STATUS** word contains various flags, including the error flag, associated with the process executing. The **Ereg** is an extra register used in

MinInt	Link 0 Output	The channel control word for the output channel on link 0
MinInt+1	Link 1 Output	The channel control word for the output channel on link 1
MinInt+2	Link 2 Output	The channel control word for the output channel on link 2
MinInt+3	Link 3 Output	The channel control word for the output channel on link 3
MinInt+4	Link 0 Input	The channel control word for the input channel on link 0
MinInt+5	Link 1 Input	The channel control word for the input channel on link 1
MinInt+6	Link 2 Input	The channel control word for the input channel on link 2
MinInt+7	Link 3 Input	The channel control word for the input channel on link 3
MinInt+8	Event	The channel control word for the event channel
MinInt+9	**TPtrLoc**$_0$	The high priority timer list pointer
MinInt+10	**TPtrLoc**$_1$	The low priority timer list pointer
MinInt+11	**Wdesc** save	Saved value of low priority **Wdesc** on interrupt
MinInt+12	**Iptr** save	Saved value of low priority **Iptr** on interrupt
MinInt+13	**Areg** save	Saved value of low priority **Areg** on interrupt
MinInt+14	**Breg** save	Saved value of low priority **Breg** on interrupt
MinInt+15	**Creg** save	Saved value of low priority **Creg** on interrupt
MinInt+16	**STATUS** save	Saved value of low priority **STATUS** word on interrupt
MinInt+17	**Ereg** save	Saved value of low priority **Ereg** on interrupt
MinInt+18 ... MinInt+27		Workspace for 2d block move — IMS T800 only

N.b. MinInt+x is a word address — i.e. x words above MinInt

Table 10.1 Special RAM locations

the block move operations.

These locations should never be written to explicitly, except when booting.

10.3   Special workspace locations

Various earlier sections have mentioned the fact that processes make use of certain locations below **Wptr** for special purposes. Also certain instructions use (**Wptr**+0) as an extra temporary 'register' to hold information while they execute. The use of these locations is described in table 10.2.

The contents of these locations only contain valid information under certain conditions. These are

   (**Wptr**−1) The process has been descheduled

   (**Wptr**−2) The process is on a scheduling list
              — i.e. has been descheduled and then rescheduled

   (**Wptr**−3) The process is waiting for communication or is executing an **ALT** construct

   (**Wptr**−4) The process is on a timer list

   (**Wptr**−5) The process is on a timer list

(**Wptr**+0)	This is used as a temporary 'register' by *outbyte*, *outword*, *postnormsn*. It is also used in the implementation of an **ALT** construct to hold the address of the selected process in the execution of the **ALT**
(**Wptr**−1)	The **Iptr** of a descheduled process is stored in this location
(**Wptr**−2)	This contains the address of the workspace of the next process in a scheduling list
(**Wptr**−3)	When a process is descheduled because it is waiting for a communication this address contains the address of the channel being used. During the execution of an **ALT** construct this contains the *ALT* state
(**Wptr**−4)	This contains the address of the workspace of the next process in a timer list or the state of time selection during an **ALT** involving timer guards
(**Wptr**−5)	This contains the time that a process on a timer list is waiting for

Table 10.2 Special locations below **Wptr**

10.4   Channel communication

This section describes the mechanism used to implement channel communication. The cases where the communication is on an internal channel and on an external channel will be considered separately. These two cases can be distinguished by looking at the channels address.

As has been described earlier, each channel has a control word in memory. This should be initialised to *NotProcess.p* when the channel is declared. The address of the channel control word is passed to the communication instruction in a register.

10.4.1   Internal communication

This occurs when two processes on the same processor wish to communicate. Because a transputer is only executing one process at any time one of these two processes will become ready to communicate first.

When the first process to become ready to communicate executes its communication instruction the transputer will find the value *NotProcess.p* in the channel control word — this signifies that the other process is not ready to communicate.

The process then

- Copies its process id (**Wdesc**) into the channel word.

- Copies the source or destination address of the communication into (**Wptr**−3) .

- Deschedules itself.

The second process to become ready to communicate executes its communication instruction. The transputer reads the value in the channel control word and finds the value is not *NotProcess.p* — and it interprets the value as the workspace address of the process that is waiting to communicate with it.

The second process then

- Performs a block move using its source or destination address, its length, and the destination or source address in the workspace pointed to by the channel control word.

- Resets the value of the channel control word to *NotProcess.p*.

- Reschedules the first process.

Note that no checking is made that the lengths of the two communications are equal — or even that they are in opposite directions. A compiler must, and can, perform this checking.

10.4.2   External communication

This occurs when processes on two different transputers wish to communicate along a link channel. The transputer can detect that communication is to take place along a link channel by examining the address of the channel control word.

Output to an external channel

When an output communication instruction is executed the value of **Wdesc**, the pointer to the message source and the message length are copied into registers in the link hardware, and the process is descheduled. The value of **Wdesc** is also copied into the relevant link channel control word — but this is to aid analysing only.

The link then extracts the message, a word at a time, from memory and transmits it byte by byte along the link. After each byte has been sent the link hardware waits for it to be acknowledged.

When all the message has been output and the final acknowledge received, the process is rescheduled and the link channel control word reset to *NotProcess.p*.

Input from an external channel

When the input communication instruction is executed the value of **Wdesc**, the pointer to the message destination and the message length are copied into registers in the link hardware, and the process is descheduled. The value of **Wdesc** is also copied into the relevant link channel control word — but this is to aid analysing only.

The link hardware then inputs bytes from the link, acknowledging each individually. These bytes are buffered up into words before being written to memory.

When all the message has been input and the final acknowledge received the process is rescheduled and the link channel control word reset to *NotProcess.p*.

As with internal communication, compilers should check that communications along external channels are of the same length.

10.4.3   Rescheduling after communication

When a communication completes — either from an internal channel or external channel — the waiting process is placed on the end of the relevant scheduling list. The priority of this process can be determined by looking at the bottom bit of its **Wdesc**. If the waiting process was a high priority process and the transputer is currently running a low priority process then the waiting process will interrupt the low priority process.

10.5   Execution of an ALT construct

Earlier, the code necessary to implement an **ALT** construct was described. This section describes what changes are made to the locations below **Wptr** and to the channel words during the execution of this construct.

The three phases of enabling, waiting and disabling are considered separately.

The *ALT* state of the alternative, held in (**Wptr**−3), has one of the following values

$$
\begin{aligned}
Enabling.p &= MostNeg+1 \\
Waiting.p &= MostNeg+2 \\
Ready.p &= MostNeg+3
\end{aligned}
$$

These values are not valid addresses of input channels. Hence an outputting process is able to distinguish between an unconditional input and an alternative input on the channel.

In addition the timer list link, held in (**Wptr**−4), has one of the following values

$$
\begin{aligned}
TimeSet.p &= MostNeg+1 \\
TimeNotSet.p &= MostNeg+2
\end{aligned}
$$

Also the value

$$
NoneSelected.o = -1
$$

is used during the disabling sequence to indicate no branch has been selected.

10.5.1   Enabling

An alternative is enabling between the execution of the *alt* or *talt* instruction and the start of the execution of the *altwt* or *taltwt* instruction.

The *ALT* state, (**Wptr**−3), is set to *Enabling.p* to indicate that the guards of an alternative construct are being enabled. If any guard is immediately ready — i.e. is a **SKIP** guard or a channel guard on a ready channel — then this location is set to *Ready.p* to indicate that a guard is ready.

Timer alternatives

A record of the earliest timer guard time yet encountered is kept during the enabling sequence of a timer alternative. Location (**Wptr**−4) contains *TimeNotSet.p* until the first timer guard is enabled and then it contains *TimeSet.p* with (**Wptr**−5) containing the earliest time encountered.

10.5.2   Waiting

An alternative is waiting between the start of execution of the *altwt* or *taltwt* instruction and the start of the next instruction. When one of the alternative guards becomes ready the process executing the alternative is rescheduled. The waiting period ends when this process comes to the front of its scheduling list and starts to execute.

The alternative selection location, (**Wptr**+0), is set to *NoneSelected.o* to indicate that no branch has yet been selected. If the *ALT* state, (**Wptr**−3), is not *Ready.p* then it is set to *Waiting.p* and the process is descheduled. Any communication to a waiting alternative causes the *ALT* state to be set to *Ready.p*

Timer alternatives

An additional check is made to see if the earliest enabled time is earlier than the current time. If so the process is not descheduled and the *ALT* state is set to *Ready.p* as a timer guard is ready. If a guard is ready then the current time is recorded in (**Wptr**−5) to indicate when the timer wait finished waiting. If no guard is ready then the process is descheduled and inserted into the appropriate timer queue.

10.5.3   Disabling

An alternative is disabling between the execution of the instruction after the *altwt* or *taltwt* instruction and the execution of the *altend* instruction.

When a guard becomes ready the disabling sequence is executed. When the first ready guard is disabled its process descriptor is stored in (**Wptr**+0) to indicate that it has been selected.

Timer alternatives

If necessary, the current process is removed from the appropriate timer queue.

10.5.4   Communication to an enabled alternative input

Outputting to an enabled alternative input is slightly different to the unconditional case. Here, although there is a valid process descriptor in the channel word, the communication does not occur as the guard has not been selected yet. Instead the outputting process puts its own process descriptor in the channel word to indicate it is ready for communication, and then deschedules itself as if the input was not ready.

10.6   CPU/FPU interface

A basic description of how the floating point unit and the main processors run concurrently has already been given. For simplicity it is always possible to consider the instruction stream being executed sequentially on one processor that performs both the integer and floating point arithmetic but to obtain even higher floating point performance it is necessary to understand the concurrency that is possible.

The two processors can be considered as occam processes communicating over channels as has already been described. To maximise the amount of overlapping between the integer and floating point processors more details of how these communications take place are needed.

The floating point instructions fall into two distinct classes. The first class operate purely on the floating point unit — such as *fpadd* — and make no change to the main processor state. The second are the instructions that can transfer data from the floating point unit to the integer processor. This second class mainly return boolean values into **Areg** — although it also includes *fpchkerr* and *fpstnlsn* and other instructions that interact with the error flag or memory.

All floating point instructions are decoded on the main processor which then waits until the floating point unit is not busy. The main processor will then send the instruction across to the floating point unit to start that operation. If the instruction is one of the first class of instructions then the main processor is free to continue to work. If it is one of the second class the main processor waits until it receives a value back from the floating point unit. In these cases there is no possibility of making use of the time while the floating point unit is operating. The occam program shown in figure 10.1 more closely models what is happening. For simplicity only single length real numbers are considered and the prefixing sequences to generate operation codes are ignored.

```
CHAN OF REAL32 databus.to.fpu, databus.from.fpu :
CHAN OF fpu.commands instruction.to.fpu :
CHAN OF BOOL result.from.fpu :
PAR
  REAL32 FAreg, FBreg, FCreg :
  WHILE TRUE
    INT inst :
    SEQ
      instruction.to.fpu ? inst
      CASE inst
        fload
          SEQ
            FCreg := FBreg
            FBreg := FAreg
            databus.to.fpu ? FAreg
        fstore
          SEQ
            databus.from.fpu ! FAreg
            FAreg := FBreg
            FBreg := FCreg
        fadd
          SEQ
            FAreg := FAreg + FBreg
            FBreg := FCreg
        feq
          SEQ
            result.from.fpu ! (FAreg = FBreg)
            FAreg := FCreg
        ... remainder of floating point unit operations
  [memsize]INT memory :
  INT Areg, Breg, Creg, Iptr :
  WHILE TRUE
    CASE memory[Iptr]
      fpldnlsn
        SEQ
          instruction.to.fpu ! fload
          databus.to.fpu ! memory[Areg]
          Areg := Breg
          Breg := Creg
          Iptr := Iptr + 1
      fpstnlsn
        SEQ
          instruction.to.fpu ! fstore
          databus.from.fpu ? memory[Areg]
          Areg := Breg
          Breg := Creg
          Iptr := Iptr + 1
      fpadd
        SEQ
          instruction.to.fpu ! fadd
          Iptr := Iptr + 1
      fpeq
        SEQ
          instruction.to.fpu ! feq
          Creg := Breg
          Breg := Areg
          result.from.fpu ? Areg
          Iptr := Iptr + 1
      ... remainder of main processor instructions
```

Figure 10.1 Occam model of CPU/FPU interface

11 Hints and tricks

This chapter details some mechanisms for optimising the performance of compiled code.

11.1 Optimising use of on-chip RAM

The on-chip RAM on a transputer provides 1 cycle memory — this is significantly faster than external memory. To get the best possible performance out of a transputer it is necessary to use this fast memory efficiently.

It is most important that on-chip RAM is used for workspace, where possible. This will reduce the access time to local variables by a factor of about 3 — depending on the speed of the external memory system. Workspace should be put in on-chip RAM in preference to code as the transputer's prefetch mechanism reduces the delay in 'visible' memory access for code fetching.

If the placing of workspace in on-chip RAM is not feasible then the most commonly used procedures etc should be placed in on-chip RAM.

11.1.1 Use of a second stack

All code described so far has used the process workspace to hold all the local variables. Initially this may seem sensible — variables are accessed quickly through local loads and stores — but problems arise when arrays are considered. A single array may take up a large number of workspace slots. This has several implications. Firstly, access to variables stored above the array may be slowed down by the need for an extra prefixing instruction to form the offset. Secondly, and more importantly, the workspace will be much larger — in particular this may mean that it cannot be placed on on-chip RAM.

This problem can be overcome by maintaining a second stack — in external memory — containing the arrays. This can be implemented as a rising stack with the address of the top of this stack being passed as an additional parameter to all procedures.

A vector declaration

        [S] INT x:

is compiled by

        ldl vector_stack; ldlp x_offset; stl x

Where x_offset is the offset from the current processes vector stack base to where x will be stored — i.e. the size of all vectors already declared by the process.

The compiler will need to statically allocate areas of the vector stack for each process in a **PAR** construct in a similar manner to the static allocation of workspaces.

Passing the vector stack pointer

When a procedure is called the address of the next free location on the vector stack is passed as the vector stack pointer. This should be passed as the second parameter to the procedure. In general it will be easier to evaluate the vector stack pointer than an 'actual' parameter. Passing it as a parameter to the *call* instruction enables the 'actual' parameters to be evaluated when more registers are available.

Array access, such as

> **x** [*E*]

is now compiled to

> *ldl x; E; wsub*

11.2   Tables of constants

The transputer instruction set has been optimised to execute the loading of small constants efficiently — for example it allows constants between 0 and 15 to be loaded in a single cycle. Analysis of programs shows that such small constants occur markedly more frequently than large constants. However when a large constant does need to be loaded the necessary prefix sequence may be long — needing 8 bytes, and hence 8 cycles, for a 32 bit constant. Other techniques may be more efficient in these cases.

A simple mechanism to increase the efficiency and code compactness is to use a table of constants. This is implemented by storing all the long constants into a lookup table. The address of this table is held in a local variable which is used to index the array — this table must be aligned on a word boundary. Then to load the constant from the nth entry in the constant table stored at address *constants* the following code would be used

> *ldl constants; ldnl n*

ldnl is the load non-local instruction which loads from a word address offset from **Areg** and is explained more fully in a later section. This code sequence could only take 2 bytes, and even in the presence of more than 16 local variables and 16 long constants it is unlikely to take more than 4 bytes.

If a constant would take 4 or more bytes to load with a *ldc* then this mechanism often improves code compactness — especially if the constant is used more than once.

If the constant table address is stored in on-chip RAM this technique can also improve performance as less code needs to be executed. If it is not stored in on-chip RAM then the extra memory cycles may cause the performance to decrease.

11.3   Implementing the occam error modes

occam supports 3 levels of error handling. These are

> **Halt**   In this mode any error causes the transputer to halt. This is useful when debugging programs so that the state that caused the error can be examined.

> **Stop**   In this mode any error in a process causes the process to be stopped. This provides for 'graceful degradation' of the system where processes continue until they become dependant on already stopped processes.

> **Reduced** In this mode nothing can be assumed about the behaviour when errors occur. In general this mode is implemented for maximum efficiency and errors may, or may not, be detected or handled. Programs run in this mode should already have been shown to be error free.

Previous sections have described how to error check expressions, array accesses etc. These cause the error flag to be set when an error occurs. Mechanisms for implementing the 3 modes above are now given. It is assumed that when error checking is performed the error flag is cleared before the expression/array access is evaluated, and that no time slicing can occur during that evaluation. This is because the error flag is not saved when a process is descheduled.

11.3.1   Halt on error

This is achieved by setting the transputer's halt on error flag by

sethalterr

This will cause the transputer to halt whenever the error flag moves from an unset to a set state.

11.3.2   Stop on error

The instruction

stoperr

is placed at the end of each error checked evaluation. This causes the process to be stopped — descheduled and not placed on the scheduling lists — if the error flag is set. This does not clear the error flag.

11.3.3   Reduced mode

In this mode all error checking instructions may be removed. In particular all *mul* instructions can be replaced by *prod* instructions to take advantage of the early termination of *prod*.

11.3.4   Error checking floating point expressions

Error checking floating point expressions is slightly more complex as floating point unit instructions affect the floating point error flag which can then be OR-ed into the main error flag to achieve error checking. The two simplest schemes in which floating point arithmetic is either all done without error checking — i.e. relying on the IEEE standard to cope with 'errors' — or all done with error checking were described in the section on floating point arithmetic.

The full implementation in which checked and unchecked arithmetic can be mixed within an expression is more complex. Code to evaluate the expression is generated by the method described earlier. The code for each *op* now consists of an optional round mode selection, the operation instruction(s) and finally either a *fpuclrerr* for an unchecked operation or a *fpchkerr* for a checked operation. This way any error in an unchecked operation is suppressed while errors in checked operations are immediately flagged. To establish the starting state of having no error the code is preceded by a *fpuclrerr*. The instructions to store the result are added after this code is compacted.

This code is not optimal as it allows no overlap between the floating point unit and the main processor since the *fpuclrerr* or *fpchkerr* instructions cause the main processor to idle while the floating point unit performs each floating point operation. This code is optimised by the following algorithm. This treats the code for the expression as a list of code elements that are either register movement operations (reverse, loads or stores) or flag operations (*fpchkerr* or *fpuclrerr*) . The error flag operations are pushed through this list as far as

```
SEQ
    holding := code [0] -- fpuclrerr is the first element in the list
    i := 1 -- pointer into code
    j := 0 -- pointer into compacted.code
    WHILE i < len
        IF
            code [i] ∈ register-movement
                SEQ
                    compacted.code [j] := code [i]
                    j := j + 1
                    i := i + 1
            code [i] = holding
                i := i + 1
            (holding = fpuclrerr) AND (code [i] = fpchkerr)
                i := i + 1
            (holding = fpchkerr) AND (code [i] = fpuclrerr)
                SEQ
                    i := i + 1
                    compacted.code [j] := fpchkerr
                    j := j + 1
                    holding := fpuclrerr
            code [i] ∈ operation
                IF
                    code [i+1] = holding
                        SEQ
                            compacted.code [j] := code [i]
                            i := i + 1
                            j := j + 1
                    TRUE
                        SEQ
                            compacted.code [j] := holding
                            compacted.code [j+1] := code [i]
                            holding := code [i+1]
                            i := i + 2
                            j := j + 2
```

Figure 11.1 Algorithm to compact floating point error checking instructions

possible maintaining the same results. The following rules are used.

flag-operation; register-movement	=	register-movement; flag-operation
fpuclrerr; fpchkerr	=	fpuclrerr
fpuclrerr; fpuclrerr	=	fpuclrerr
fpchkerr; fpchkerr	=	fpchkerr
fpchkerr; operation; fpchkerr	=	operation; fpchkerr
fpuclrerr; operation; fpuclrerr	=	operation; fpuclrerr

An algorithm to compact the use of floating point error checking instructions is shown in figure 11.1. The algorithm uses set membership ∈ in its IF conditionals to aid clarity. In an implementation these would be replaced by the relevant equality conditionals. The algorithm assumes that the expression has been compiled into the area *code* and has length *len*. The algorithm generates the result in the array *compacted.code*. The last error flag operation is left in *holding* and should be held over until after the address of the destination of the evaluated expression has been calculated. This will maximise the overlap of the last operation. The error flag operation should be inserted before the store instruction. This gives the processor a chance to halt on error before possibly overwriting data. If the processor is halted then the values of all data used in the expression can be analysed as none will have been over-written.

Using this algorithm all the error flag operations are pushed through the code as far as they will go. The variable *holding* is used to hold the most recent flag operation whose execution is being deferred. In most cases this will delay the synchronisation needed to check the error flag until just before synchronisation is required for an operation — so there will be no time lost due to 'redundant' synchronisations.

To show how this works consider the code to evaluate the expression

```
X := (A + B) TIMES (C + D)
```

where the + operations are to be error checked but the **TIMES** is unchecked multiplication. All the variables are assumed to be **REAL32**s. The naive code for this is

fpuclrerr; ldlp A; fpldnlsn; ldlp B; fpldnlsn; fpadd; fpchkerr;
ldlp C; fpldnlsn; ldlp D; fpldnlsn; fpadd; fpchkerr; fpmul; fpuclrerr

When compacted the initial *fpuclrerr* is moved over the first two register movements to just before the *fpadd*. The *fpchkerr* is moved up to the next *fpadd* where — because the *fpadd* is followed by another *fpchkerr* — it is dropped. The second *fpchkerr* is not moved over the *fpmul* so that it will catch any errors caused by the two *fpadd*s. The second *fpuclrerr* can be dropped as the value left in the error flag by this evaluation should not be being used outside of the actual evaluation.

The resulting code therefore is

ldlp A; fpldnlsn; ldlp B; fpldnlsn; fpuclrerr; fpadd;
ldlp C; fpldnlsn; ldlp D; fpldnlsn; fpadd; fpchkerr; fpmul

which can be further compacted by using *fpldnladdsn* instead of *fpldnlsn; fpadd*.

11.4   Optimising floating point performance

Since the IMS T800 consists of two concurrently operating processor units which only synchronise on data transfer between them there is much scope to optimise performance by balancing the amount of work performed on these two units.

For a floating point intensive application the work consists of both the actual floating point calculations and the loading and storing of data for these calculations. On an IMS T800 the floating point unit performs all the floating point calculations while the integer processor calculates the address of the data to be loaded into and stored from the floating point unit. To optimise performance the code needs to ensure that the integer processor is not sitting idle waiting for the floating point unit to synchronise when there is enough spare time to do some useful work. For example the following program fragment

```
[20][20] REAL64 A, B :
REAL64 C,D :
SEQ
  ...
  A [I][J] := (B [I][J] * C) + D
```

integer unit	cycles		floating point unit	cycles
genaddr(B [I][J])	18		(idle)	18
fpldnldb	5	—synchronisation—	fpldnldb	5
genaddr(C)	1		idle	1
fpldnldb	5	—synchronisation—	fpldnldb	5
fpmul	2	—synchronisation—	fpmul	20
genaddr(D)	1			
idle	17			
fpldnldb	5	—synchronisation—	fpldnldb	5
fpadd	2	—synchronisation—	fpadd	7
genaddr(A [I][J])	18		idle	13
fpstnldb	5	—synchronisation—	fpstnldb	5
Total time	79			
Idle time	17			14

Figure 11.2 Execution profile of unoptimised code

could be naively coded as

>   genaddr(B [I][J]); fpldnldb; genaddr(C); fpldnldb; fpmul;
>   genaddr(D); fpldnldb; fpadd; genaddr(A [I][J]); fpstnldb

where *genaddr(X)* is the code required to generate the address of the variable *X*.

The effect of this is is shown in figure 11.2.

Unless otherwise stated all examples in this section assume that all data is stored in internal RAM and that all simple variables are locally declared while arrays are accessed through one level of static linkage. The overlap assumed here has been simplified slightly to aid understanding of the example. In reality the first two cycles of a synchronising instruction on the integer processor overlap as well.

The initial 18 cycles while the first two addresses are being calculated are not included in the total of the floating point unit's idle time as in theory these could be overlapped with the last operation of the previous assignment.

A more intelligent approach to code generation for this process would notice the length of time 'free' while the floating point unit did the *fpmul* and use it to precompute another address. This could cause the following code to be generated.

>   genaddr(C); genaddr(B [I][J]); fpldnldb; fpldnldb; fpmul;
>   genaddr(A [I][J]); genaddr(D); fpldnldb; fpadd; fpstnldb

The profile of this code sequence is shown in figure 11.3.

Now the floating point unit has been almost saturated — once the initial pair of values have been loaded into the floating point unit it is only idle for 1 cycle — so for the available hardware the evaluation is well optimised. This has made a 23% improvement in the performance.

For larger expressions and sequences of expressions some of the remaining idle time could be used. The initial 19 cycles idle time on the floating point unit can be decreased by overlapping the initial address calculation with the last operation of an immediately previous assignment if the compiler allows code to be

integer unit	cycles		floating point unit	cycles
genaddr(C)	1		(idle)	1
genaddr(B [I][J])	18		(idle)	18
fpldnldb	5	—synchronisation—	*fpldnldb*	5
fpldnldb	5	—synchronisation—	*fpldnldb*	5
fpmul	2	—synchronisation—	*fpmul*	20
genaddr(A [I][J])	18			
genaddr(D)	1		idle	1
fpldnldb	5	—synchronisation—	*fpldnldb*	5
fpadd	2	—synchronisation—	*fpadd*	7
idle	5			
fpstnldb	5	—synchronisation—	*fpstnldb*	5
Total time	64			
Idle time	5			1

Figure 11.3 Execution profile of optimised code

moved over statement boundaries.

11.4.1   Optimising code

The main factor that introduces unnecessary delays into floating point code is unoverlapped address evaluation. Code to evaluate an expression can be generated using the standard depth-first methods described earlier. There are then a few very simple 'transformations' that can be made on the code to maximise the overlap. In the following definitions *genaddr* will be a section of code to generate an address on the integer processor, *trans* will be an instruction to transfer data to or from the floating point unit and *op* will be a floating point operation. Error flag and rounding mode operations are treated as part of the instruction that they immediately precede.

The first optimisation is to delay the synchronisation in sequences of transfer operations. In a sequence such as

$$genaddr_1; \ trans_1; \ genaddr_2; \ trans_2$$

$genaddr_1$ may be overlapped with a prior floating point operation, but $trans_1$ causes synchronisation so that $genaddr_2$ is not overlapped — i.e. the floating point unit will be idle here. The following two transformations maximise the overlap of address generation in all such cases. These transformations enable the overhead of storing subresults to temporaries during complicated expression evaluations to be minimised.

$$1. \ genaddr_1; \ trans_1; \ genaddr_2; \ trans_2; \ genaddr_3$$
$$= genaddr_3; \ genaddr_2; \ genaddr_1; \ trans_1; \ trans_2$$

$$2. \ genaddr_1; \ trans_1; \ genaddr_2 = genaddr_2; \ genaddr_1; \ trans_1$$

When the compiler generates the code for $genaddr_n$ sequences it must take account of the depth of stack needed to compile each expression. Previous sections show how to compile optimal code for any combination of the depths of the evaluations. However in the case of address generation here it may be simpler to associate with each generation the number of elements on the stack it needs to preserve. This is needed to make the next transformation easier to implement. A later stage of the compiler can then use temporary storage if necessary to avoid stack overflow — in the case where the $genaddr_n$s are contiguous the scheme to load registers with integer operands given in the section on sequential processes can be used. The first of the two

```
                 1. op₁; op₂; genaddr₁; genaddr₂ =
                 IF
                     op₁ = fpadd/fpsub
                        IF
                           quick(genaddr₁)
                              op₁; genaddr₁; op₂; genaddr₂
                           quick(genaddr₂)
                              op₁; genaddr₂; op₂; genaddr₁; rev
                           TRUE
                              op₁; genaddr₁; op₂; genaddr₂
                     op₂ = fpadd/fpsub
                        IF
                           quick(genaddr₂)
                              op₁; genaddr₁; op₂; genaddr₂
                           quick(genaddr₁)
                              op₁; genaddr₂; op₂; genaddr₁; rev
                           TRUE
                              op₁; genaddr₁; op₂; genaddr₂
                     TRUE
                        op₁; genaddr₁; op₂; genaddr₂

                 2. op₁; op₂; genaddr; trans =
                 IF
                     op₁ = fpmul/fpdiv
                        op₁; genaddr; op₂; trans
                     TRUE
                        op₁; op₂; genaddr; trans

                 3. op₁; genaddr₁; trans; op₂; genaddr₂ =
                 IF
                     op₁ = fpmul/fpdiv ∧ op₂ = fpadd/fpsub ∧
                              quick(genaddr₁) ∧ ¬quick(genaddr₂)
                        op₁; genaddr₂; genaddr₁; trans; op₂
                     TRUE
                        op₁; genaddr₁; trans; op₂; genaddr₂
```

Figure 11.4 Optmising address generation

transformations above can be obtained by two applications of the second but probably should be implemented separately so that the details of how many addresses are being held on the integer stack can be dealt with more simply.

The second optimisation is to reorder address generations so that 'quick' evaluations overlap floating point additions or subtractions. Generating the address of a simple variable or of an element of a 1 dimensional array are both considered to be 'quick' as each will (usually) overlap totally with a floating point addition or subtraction. Accesses to 2 or higher dimensional arrays usually take at least as long as a floating point multiplication or division. To maximise the overlap of address generations the transformations in figure 11.4 should be used.

The first of these three transformations will move a 'quick' address evaluation — where possible — so that it overlaps a floating point addition or subtraction rather than a multiplication or division. The second ensures that if only one address is to be generated then it overlaps a multiplication or division where possible. The third enables a 'long' address calculations to be overlapped with multiplications or divisions.

If $genaddr_1$ and $genaddr_2$ are swapped by the first or third transformations then the number of elements on the stack that need to be preserved by each must be swapped — i.e. the number of elements to be preserved is associated with the position of the address generation rather than with the actual address generation.

11.4.2   Efficiency of optimisations

The optimisations detailed above should be fairly easy to incorporate in a compiler. Other optimisations involving reordering the actual compiled code are probably not worth the cost in compiler complexity.

The optimisations above have been attempted on some 'typical' scientific program fragments written in occam. The results showed about a 5% increase in performance for programs using scalar variables or 1-dimensional arrays, while when 2-dimensional arrays were used the performance increase was between 20% and 30% due to the presence of more work in array element access that could be overlapped.

Appendices

A   IEEE floating point format

Values in the **REAL32** and **REAL64** formats are stored in the following formats

where *s* is the sign bit, *exp* is the exponent and *frac* is the fraction. For the **REAL32** type *s* is 1 bit wide, *exp* is 8 bits wide and *frac* is 23 bits wide. For the **REAL64** type *s* is 1 bit wide, *exp* is 11 bits wide and *frac* is 52 bits wide. Whenever the *exp* field is not 0 the actual fraction of the number represented has an 'implied' 1 placed on the left of the *frac* value.

The value of finite **REAL**s is given by

$$val \boxed{\;s\;|\;exp\;|\;frac\;} = \begin{cases} (-1)^s \times 1.frac \times 2^{exp-bias}, & \text{if } exp \neq 0; \\ (-1)^s \times 0.frac \times 2^{1-bias}, & \text{if } exp = 0; \end{cases}$$

where *bias* is 127 for **REAL32** and 1023 for **REAL64**

B   Compliance with the IEEE 754 standard

INMOS has produced various implementations of the IEEE 754 floating point arithmetic standard. These range from the hardware implementation of the IMS T800 to various software implementations for the IMS T414 and IMS T212. All implementations have been designed to produce the same results so that applications can be run on different transputers yet produce the same results.

B.1   The IEEE standard and INMOS implementations

The INMOS implementations are intended to provide IEEE 754 floating point arithmetic inside occam processes. The implementations have been designed to comply with the IEEE 754 standard as closely as possible and to perform correctly all the arithmetic and conversion operations with a full implementation of Not-a-Numbers and denormalised numbers. Since transputers are optimised for running high level languages, such as occam, it is important that the design reflects the requirements of these languages. This has meant that certain parts of the IEEE standard are not supported in hardware. Principally these are the concepts of exceptions and traps. The IEEE 754 standard is basically a hardware standard and incorporating the full standard into a rigorous software environment, such as occam, is difficult.

The INMOS floating point implementations perform all arithmetic operations, conversions and comparisons correctly according to the standard in both single and double length formats. Invalid operation, division by zero and overflow exceptions can be made to cause a process to halt. In this way they implement all of the IEEE 754 standard apart from exceptions and traps which are handled in a different way.

The full IEEE 754 standard can be implemented using software support. This fully meets the requirements of the standard but it is not expected that anyone would ever use it as the INMOS implementation provides all that 'normal' users require.

The compliance or otherwise of each of the INMOS implementations with the IEEE 754 standard is now detailed dealing with topics in the same order as the standard.

B.2   IMS T800

The IMS T800 has IEEE 754 floating point arithmetic implemented in hardware in the floating point unit. Most of the operations of the standard are implemented as instructions although a few are provided as short code sequences suitable for use as in-line code inserts.

B.2.1   Real formats

The single and double length formats of the IEEE standard are fully supported. The extended formats are not supported.

B.2.2   Rounding

On the IMS T800 *Round-to-Nearest* mode is the default rounding mode. Unless an instruction is explicitly preceded by a set rounding mode instruction then the instruction will use *Round-to-Nearest* mode. There is no rounding precision option as instructions either round to a definite format (e.g. round from **REAL64** to **REAL64**) or round to the format of the operands of the instruction. The infinitely precise result needed for correct rounding is provided through having a round bit below the least significant bit of the fraction and a sticky bit which contains all lower bits OR-ed together.

B.2.3   Arithmetic

Addition, subtraction, multiplication, division are implemented as instructions that act on two operands held in the **FAreg** and **FBreg** floating point registers. These operands should be of the same format — a compiler must check this as the floating point unit makes no check that the types are the same. The correctly rounded result in the same format as the operands is returned in **FAreg**. Operations on operands of different formats are not supported as this would contravene the type checking rules of occam. If *single op double* is required then a simple type conversion is needed — *(DOUBLE single) op double*.

B.2.4   Square root

Square root is implemented by a short code sequence which returns a result in the same format as the argument.

B.2.5   Conversions

Conversions between two of the integer types supported in occam (**INT32** and **INT64**) and the two real formats are provided along with the *'round floating point number to integer value'* required by the IEEE standard. These are implemented by various code sequences and instructions. In conversions to integer, an integer overflow caused the floating point error to be set.

B.2.6   Binary/decimal conversions

These are provided by occam procedures in which a decimal value in a **BYTE** array can be converted into the **REALxx** that it represents and vice versa.

B.2.7   Comparisons

Two instructions implement > and = in a form that does not distinguish between finite numbers, infinities and Not-a-Numbers. They treat infinities and Not-a-Numbers as being normalised numbers with an exponent of MaxExp. In this way the IEEE floating point numbers are ordered

> Not-a-Numbers with sign bit set $<$ − infinity $<$ finite numbers
> $<$ + infinity $<$ Not-a-Numbers with sign bit clear

Unorderedness can also be obtained through another instruction, so from these 3 primitives all of the comparisons in the IEEE standard can be constructed. In particular IEEE greater than and equal to are available as short code sequences.

B.2.8   Not-a-Numbers

Several Not-a-Numbers are produced by the floating point unit to signify the various invalid operations that are possible. These Not-a-Numbers all propagate through arithmetic in the ways specified in the IEEE standard. If an operation has two Not-a-Numbers as operands then the 'larger' Not-a-Number is returned. The presence of a Not-a-Number as an input or output to an operation causes an error to be returned which enables the signalling of Not- a-Numbers to be implemented. Such an error causes the floating point error flag on the IMS T800 to be set

The Not-a-Numbers can be made to be quiet (propagating through expressions) or signalling (setting the main error flag, halting the processor) dependent on whether the floating error flag is OR-ed into the main error flag — i.e. depending on whether the floating point mode is check or unchecked.

B.2.9   Exceptions

Exception handling is provided through the error returned from operations. On the IMS T800 an error causes the floating point error flag to be set. This error can be copied into the transputer error flag so that exceptions can be signalled. In this area the IMS T800 implementation diverges from the full IEEE standard.

IEEE 754 stipulates that 5 types of exception shall be signalled — invalid operation, division by zero, overflow, underflow and inexact. These are signified by bits being set or unset in a status word. This could have been implemented but there were reasons against doing so when the IMS T800 was designed. It would have introduced more state into the floating point unit. To examine the contents of this register it would probably have been necessary to copy it across into the integer **Areg** and then perform masking operations on it. This would have had an impact on performance as well as losing the simplicity that had been gained on the IMS T414 of having only one error flag.

On the IMS T800 an invalid operation results in the floating point error flag being set along with the corresponding Not-a-Number being returned. Division by zero sets the floating point error flag and the correct infinity. Overflow rounds to the result as specified and sets the floating point error flag.

Underflow and inexact are not supported in any way.

In addition any operation having a Not-a-Number or an infinity as an input returns an error. The Not-a-Number case is the way in which Not-a-Numbers can be treated as signalling. The infinity case is not specified in the IEEE standard but the signalling of 'infinite' arguments seems useful. This is because a value that is an infinity is either a true infinity or just an overflow. The IEEE standard treats an overflow as if it were true infinity and hence having the same exact arithmetic properties as true infinity. This could be dangerous and it seems helpful to flag operations where an overflowed value may be being used.

If the floating point error flag is cleared at the start of each expression evaluation and is examined before the result is stored then the presence of an invalid operation, division by zero or overflow in its calculation can be detected. Also if the result is a Not-a-Number then its 'value' shows which error caused that Not-a-Number to be returned.

B.2.10   Traps

Traps are not provided.

B.3   Software implementations

occam functions and procedures to support IEEE 754 arithmetic are included in the standard compiler libraries.

REALxxOP, REALxxREM, REALxxGT, REALxxEQ, SQRT, DSQRT etc are a collection of occam functions which implement the main areas of the IEEE 754 floating point arithmetic standard. They are designed for efficient execution — other functions detailed in the next section give a fuller implementation of the standard.

REAL32OP has been optimised for the IMS T414 by making use of the microcode floating point support instructions.

B.3.1   Real formats

The single and double length formats of the IEEE standard are fully supported. The extended formats are not supported.

B.3.2   Rounding

Rounding is performed in *Round-to-Nearest* mode for the arithmetic operations. With the type conversions there is a choice between *Round-to-Nearest* mode and *Round-to-Zero* (truncation) mode. There is no rounding precision option as instructions either round to a definite format (e.g. round from **REAL64** to **REAL32**) or round to the format of the operands of the instruction. The infinitely precise result needed for correct rounding is provided through having a round bit below the least significant bit of the fraction and a sticky bit which contains all lower bits OR-ed together.

B.3.3   Arithmetic

Addition, subtraction, multiplication, division are provided by **REALxxOP**. This takes as its parameters two operands, of the same format, and a value indicating which operation is to be performed. The correctly rounded result is returned.

Similarily **REALxxREM** returns the remainder of the operands passed as parameters.

Operations on operands of different formats are performed using a type conversion in the same way as on the IMS T800.

B.3.4   Square root

Square root is provided by the **SQRT** and **DSQRT** functions in the occam standard function library.

B.3.5   Conversions

Conversions between two of the integer types supported in occam (**INT32** and **INT64**) and the two real formats are provided along with the round floating point number to integer value required by the IEEE standard through various occam functions. Integer overflow causes the transputer error flag to be set.

B.3.6   Binary/decimal conversions

These are provided by occam procedures in which a decimal value in a **BYTE** array can be converted in to the **REALxx** that it represents and vice versa.

B.3.7   Comparisons

REALxxGT and **REALxxEQ** implement > and = in a similar way to that on the IMS T800 in which finite numbers, infinities and Not-a-Numbers are not distinguised. These implement IEEE comparison correctly when both arguments are not Not-a-Numbers.

B.3.8   Not-a-Numbers

The generation and propagation of Not-a-Numbers is the same as on the IMS T800. All Not-a-Numbers are signalling in these implementations as the main transputer error flag will be set when a Not-a-Number is created.

B.3.9   Exceptions

Exception handling is as on the IMS T800 except that the main transputer error flag will be set where the IMS T800 would set the floating point error flag.

B.3.10   Traps

Traps are not provided.

B.4   Error flagging software implementations

IEEExxOP, **IEEExxREM** and **IEEExxCOMPARE** are occam functions that provide for a fuller implementation of the IEEE 754 floating point arithmetic standard.

B.4.1   Real formats

The single and double length formats of the IEEE standard are fully supported. The extended formats are not supported.

B.4.2   Rounding

All 4 rounding modes in the IEEE 754 standard are supported.

B.4.3   Arithmetic

Addition, subtractions, multiplication and division are provided by **IEEExxOP**. **IEEExxOP** takes as its parameters two operands, of the same type, a value representing the rounding mode to be used and a value indicating the operation to be used. It returns the correctly rounded result along with a **BOOL** flag. This flag is **TRUE** when the operation raised an exception.

Similarly **IEEExxREM** implements remainder and returns the correct result along with a **BOOL** flag indicating whether the remainder caused an exception to be raised.

B.4.4   Comparisons

IEEExxCOMPARE takes as its parameters two arguments of the same type and returns a value indicating whether the first argument is greater than, equal to or less than the second argument or whether the two arguments were unordered in the sense of the IEEE 754 standard. This enables all the comparisons described in the IEEE 754 standard to be implemented.

Error	Single length value	Double length value
Divide zero by zero	#7FC00000	#7FF80000 00000000
Divide infinity by infinity	#7FA00000	#7FF40000 00000000
Multiply zero by infinity	#7F900000	#7FF20000 00000000
Addition of opposite signed infinities	#7F880000	#7FF10000 00000000
Subtraction of same signed infinities	#7F880000	#7FF10000 00000000
Negative square root	#7F840000	#7FF08000 00000000
REAL64 to REAL32 NaN conversion	#7F820000	#7FF04000 00000000
Remainder from infinity	#7F804000	#7FF00800 00000000
Remainder by zero	#7F802000	#7FF00400 00000000

Figure B.1 Arithmetic Not-a-Number values

B.4.5   Not-a-Numbers

The generation and propagation of Not-a-Numbers is the same as on the IMS T800. Not-a-Numbers are quiet in these implementations as the main transputer error flag is not affected. However, the result can be examined and tested, and the error flag explicitly set, so that certain Not-a-Numbers can be made to be signalling.

B.4.6   Exceptions

Exception handling is as on the IMS T800 except that the **BOOL** result will be **TRUE** where the IMS T800 would set the floating point error flag.

B.4.7   Traps

Traps are not provided.

B.5   Full IEEE arithmetic

A full implementation of IEEE arithmetic including status registers, rounding mode registers etc. can be implemented in a mixture of software and the floating point unit hardware to give full compliance with IEEE 754.

B.6   Not-a-Number values

The INMOS floating point arithmetic software implementations and the IMS T800 return the various 'values' of Not-a-Numbers to signify the various errors that can occur in evaluations. These are shown in figure B.1.

In addition the INMOS standard function libraries return the Not-a-Number 'values' in figure B.2.

Result not defined mathematically means that the function is undefined for the argument — e.g. a logarithm of a negative number.

Result unstable and inaccurate are both caused by the inability of the algorithm to return an accurate result given the presumed inaccuracy of the argument. An unstable result is caused by the function being mathe-

Result not defined mathematically	#7F800010	#7FF00002 00000000
Result unstable	#7F800008	#7FF00001 00000000
Result inaccurate	#7F800004	#7FF00000 80000000

Figure B.2 Standard function Not-a-Number values

matically unstable. An inaccurate result is caused by the the algorithm being unable to evaluate accurately the result even though the function is well behaved. Taking the tangent of $\frac{\pi}{2}$ would result in an unstable Not-a-Number as a small error in the argument could alter the result from a very large positive number to a very large negative number. Taking the sine of a very large argument can result in an inaccurate Not-a-Number as the reduction to primary range cannot be performed accurately due to the approximation to π used in the algorithm.

C Special values

The transputer uses certain special values to store information about the sate of channel communication, alternative execution etc. These are listed in the table below.

Name	Use	32 bit value	16 bit value
MostNeg	The most negative value	#80000000	#8000
MostPos	The most positive value	#7FFFFFFF	#7FFF
NotProcess.p	Used, where a process descriptor is expected, to indicate that there is no process. In channel word shows no communication waiting, in timer queue shows end of queue	#80000000	#8000
Enabling.p	Stored in (**Wptr**−3) while alternative is being enabled.	#80000001	#8001
Waiting.p	Stored in (**Wptr**−3) while alternative is waiting.	#80000002	#8002
Disabling.p	Stored in (**Wptr**−3) while alternative is being disabled.	#80000003	#8003
TimeSet.p	Stored in (**Wptr**−4) during enabling of timer alternative after a time to wait for has been encountered.	#80000001	#8001
TimeNotSet.p	Stored in (**Wptr**−4) during enabling of timer alternative when no time to wait for has been encountered.	#80000002	#8002
NoneSelected.o	Stored in (**Wptr**+0) while no branch of an alternative has been selected during the waiting and disabling phases		

D   Instructions set summary

The instructions executed by the processor include direct functions, the prefixing functions *pfix* and *nfix*, and an indirect function *opr* which uses the operand register **Oreg** to select one of a set of operations.

The set of functions and operations is given below. These are listed in a similar order to the order in which they were introduced earlier. A list ordered by op-codes follows as an aid to debugging transputer code.

Also included is the number of processor cycles that each instruction takes to execute. This number does not include the time for any preceding prefix instructions. The following symbols are used in the timings

b	the bit number of the highest bit set in **Areg**
n	the number of bits of a shift
w	the number of words, plus non word aligned part words, in a message
bpw	the number of bits per word

The timings assume all memory access is to on chip RAM. Timings marked with a '*' indicate a worst case time. The time taken for certain instructions — especially those dealing with timer queues etc — is totally dependent on the machine state when executed so no time is given and a '†' symbol appears in the table. Note that timings for instructions that can cause descheduling, such as communication, assume that that communication proceeds immediately without the process being descheduled.

The column **D/E** contains a 'D' if the instruction can cause the current process to be descheduled and an 'E' if it can cause the error flag to be set.

D.1   Direct, prefixing and indirect functions

The **Code** given below is the contents of the code field of the instruction that occupies the most significant 4 bits of the byte. The data to the operation is placed in the least significant 4 bits of the byte with prefixing instructions being used to build data values of greater than 4 bits.

Code	Abbreviation	Cycles	D/E	
#2	pfix	1		prefix
#6	nfix	1		negative prefix
#F	opr	–		operate — *for timing see operation list*
#4	ldc	1		load constant
#7	ldl	2		load local
#D	stl	1		store local
#1	ldlp	1		load local pointer
#8	adc	1	E	add constant
#C	eqc	2		equals constant
#0	j	3	D	jump
#A	cj	4		conditional jump — *jump taken*
		2		conditional jump — *jump not taken*
#3	ldnl	2		load non local
#E	stnl	2		store non local
#5	ldnlp	1		load non local pointer
#9	call	7		call
#B	ajw	1		adjust workspace

D.2   Operations

The **Code** given below is the value that needs to be placed in the operand register for the *opr* function that performs the operation. For example a *ret*, whose code is **#20**, is executed by the code

pfix 2; opr 0

which is in hexadecimal notation

#22; #F0

A short operation can be expressed as a single byte as no prefixing is required to the *opr* instruction. A long operation requires two bytes as a prefix instruction is required.

Code	Size	Abbreviation	Cycles	D/E	
#00	short	*rev*	1		reverse
#05	short	*add*	1	E	add
#0C	short	*sub*	1	E	subtract
#53	long	*mul*	bpw+6	E	multiply
#2C	long	*div*	bpw+10*	E	divide
#1F	long	*rem*	bpw+5	E	remainder
#52	long	*sum*	1		sum
#04	short	*diff*	1		difference
#08	short	*prod*	b+4		product
#46	long	*and*	1		and
#4B	long	*or*	1		or
#33	long	*xor*	1		exclusive or
#32	long	*not*	1		bitwise not
#41	long	*shl*	n+2		shift left
#40	long	*shr*	n+2		shift right
#09	short	*gt*	2		greater than
#21	long	*lend*	10	D	loop end — *loop back*
			5		loop end — *exit loop*
#34	long	*bcnt*	2		byte count
#3F	long	*wcnt*	5		word count
#1B	long	*ldpi*	2		load pointer to instruction
#42	long	*mint*	1		mimimum integer
#02	short	*bsub*	1		byte subscript
#0A	short	*wsub*	2		word subscript
#4A	long	*move*	2w+8		move message
#07	short	*in*	2w+18		input message — *communication procedes*
			20	D	input message — *communication waits*
#07	short	*out*	2w+20		output message — *communication procedes*
			20	D	output message — *communication waits*

Code	Size	Abbreviation	Cycles	D/E	
#01	short	*lb*	5		load byte
#3B	long	*sb*	4		store byte
#0E	short	*outbyte*	25	D	output byte
#0F	short	*outword*	25	D	output word
#06	short	*gcall*	4		general call
#3C	long	*gajw*	2		general adjust workspace
#20	long	*ret*	5		return
#0D	short	*startp*	12		start process
#03	short	*endp*	13	D	end process
#39	long	*runp*	10		run process
#15	long	*stopp*	11	D	stop process
#1E	long	*ldpri*	1		load current priority
#22	long	*ldtimer*	2		load timer
#2B	long	*tin*	†	D	timer input
#43	long	*alt*	2		alt start
#44	long	*altwt*	†	D	alt wait
#45	long	*altend*	6		alt end
#4E	long	*talt*	4		timer alt start
#51	long	*taltwt*	†	D	timer alt wait
#49	long	*enbs*	3		enable skip
#30	long	*diss*	4		disable skip
#48	long	*enbc*	7*		enable channel
#2F	long	*disc*	8		disable channel
#47	long	*enbt*	8		enable timer
#2E	long	*dist*	†		disable timer
#13	long	*csub0*	2	E	check subscript from 0
#4D	long	*ccnt1*	3	E	check count from 1
#29	long	*testerr*	3*		test error false and clear
#55	long	*stoperr*	2		stop on error
#10	long	*seterr*	1	E	set error
#3A	long	*xword*	4		extend to word
#56	long	*cword*	5	E	check word
#1D	long	*xdble*	2		extend to double
#4C	long	*csngl*	3	E	check single
#16	long	*ladd*	2	E	long add
#38	long	*lsub*	2	E	long subtract
#37	long	*lsum*	2		long sum
#4F	long	*ldiff*	2		long diff
#31	long	*lmul*	bpw+1		long multiply
#1A	long	*ldiv*	bpw+3	E	long divide
#36	long	*lshl*	n+3		long shift left
#35	long	*lshr*	n+3		long shift right
#19	long	*norm*	bpw+5*		normalise

Code	Size	Abbreviation	Cycles	D/E	
#12	long	*resetch*	3		reset channel
#2A	long	*testpranal*	2		test processor analysing
#18	long	*sthf*	1		store high priority front pointer
#1C	long	*stlf*	1		store low priority front pointer
#54	long	*sttimer*	1		store timer
#50	long	*sthb*	1		store high priority back pointer
#17	long	*stlb*	1		store low priority back pointer
#3E	long	*saveh*	4		save high priority queue registers
#3D	long	*savel*	4		save low priority queue registers
#57	long	*clrhalterr*	1		clear halt-on-error
#58	long	*sethalterr*	1		set halt-on-error
#59	long	*testhalterr*	2		test halt-on-error

D.3   Extra instructions on 32 bit transputers

Code	Size	Abbreviation	Cycles	D/E	
#72	long	*fmul*	40	E	fractional multiply

D.4   Extra instructions on IMS T414

Code	Size	Abbreviation	Cycles	D/E	
#63	long	*unpacksn*	16		unpack single length fp number
#6D	long	*roundsn*	15		round single length fp number
#6C	long	*postnormsn*	30*		post-normalise correction of single length fp number
#71	long	*ldinf*	1		load single length infinity
#73	long	*cflerr*	3	E	check single length fp infinity or NaN

D.5   Additional instructions on IMS T800

D.5.1   Main processor instructions

Code	Size	Abbreviation	Cycles	D/E
#5A	long	*dup*	1	duplicate top of stack
#5B	long	*move2dinit*	†	initialise data for 2 dimensional block move
#5C	long	*move2dall*	†	2 dimensional block copy
#5D	long	*move2dnonzero*	†	2 dimensional block copy non zero bytes
#5E	long	*move2dzero*	†	2 dimensional block copy zero bytes
#74	long	*crcword*	bpw+3	calculate CRC on word
#75	long	*crcbyte*	11	calculate CRC on byte
#76	long	*bitcnt*	b+2	count bits set in word
#77	long	*bitrevword*	bpw+4	reverse bits in word
#78	long	*bitrevnbits*	n+4	reverse bottom n bits in word
#81	long	*wsubdb*	3	form double word subscript

D.5.2   Floating point unit instructions

The time taken to execute many floating point instructions is extremely data dependent. The timings given here are typical times for such instructions, such as arithmetic on normalised data. Certain values in the registers may cause execution to take more or less time. For the multiply and divide instructions two values are given, first for single length data and then for double length. The number of cycles quoted does not take account of any prefixing sequences or the loading of an op code into **Areg** for an *fpentry* instruction. The column **F** contains an entry 'F' if the instruction can cause the floating point error flag to be set.

A floating point instruction whose **Size** is described as being 'seq' is executed by loading its **Code** into **Areg** then executing an *fpentry* instruction.

Code	Size	Abbreviation	Cycles	F
#AB	long	*fpentry*	–	F	floating point unit entry
#A3	long	*fpdup*	1		floating point duplicate
#A4	long	*fprev*	1		floating point reverse
#8E	long	*fpldnlsn*	3		floating point load non local single
#8A	long	*fpldnldb*	5		floating point load non local double
#86	long	*fpldnlsni*	5		floating point load non local indexed single
#82	long	*fpldnldbi*	7		floating point load non local indexed double
#88	long	*fpstnlsn*	3		floating point store non local single
#84	long	*fpstnldb*	5		floating point store non local double
#22	seq	*fpurn*	1		set rounding mode to round nearest
#06	seq	*fpurz*	1		set rounding mode to round zero
#04	seq	*fpurp*	1		set rounding mode to round positive
#05	seq	*fpurm*	1		set rounding mode to round minus

Code	Size	Abbreviation	Cycles	F	
#87	long	*fpadd*	7	F	floating point add
#89	long	*fpsub*	7	F	floating point subtract
#8B	long	*fpmul*	11|20	F	floating point multiply
#8C	long	*fpdiv*	17|32	F	floating point divide
#01	seq	*fpusqrtfirst*	25	F	floating point square root first step
#02	seq	*fpusqrtstep*	42		floating point square root step
#03	seq	*fpusqrtlast*	10		floating point square root end
#8F	long	*fpremfirst*	48*	F	floating point remainder first step
#90	long	*fpremstep*	40*		floating point remainder iteration step
#9F	long	*fpldzerosn*	1		load zero single
#A0	long	*fpldzerodb*	1		load zero double
#12	seq	*fpumulby2*	8	F	multiply by 2.0
#11	seq	*fpudivby2*	8	F	divide by 2.0
#0A	seq	*fpuexpinc32*	8	F	multiply by 2^{32}
#09	seq	*fpuexpdec32*	8	F	divide by 2^{32}
#0B	seq	*fpuabs*	2	F	floating point absolute
#AA	long	*fpldnladdsn*	10	F	floating point load non local and add single
#A6	long	*fpldnladddb*	12	F	floating point load non local and add double
#AC	long	*fpldnlmulsn*	14	F	floating point load non local and multiply single
#A8	long	*fpldnlmuldb*	25	F	floating point load non local and multiply double
#83	long	*fpchkerr*	2		check floating point error
#9C	long	*fptesterr*	2		test floating point error false and clear
#23	seq	*fpuseterr*	1	F	set floating point error
#9C	seq	*fpuclrerr*	1		clear floating point error
#94	long	*fpgt*	5	F	floating point greater than
#95	long	*fpeq*	4	F	floating point equality
#92	long	*fpordered*	4		floating point orderability
#91	long	*fpnan*	3		floating point nan
#93	long	*fpnotfinite*	2		floating point finite
#07	seq	*fpur32tor64*	3	F	real32 to real64
#08	seq	*fpur64tor32*	5	F	real64 to real32
#A1	long	*fpint*	6	F	round to floating integer
#9E	long	*fpstnli32*	4		store non local int32
#0E	seq	*fpuchki32*	4	F	check in range of type int32
#0F	seq	*fpuchki64*	4	F	check in range of type int64
#9D	long	*fprtoi32*	10	F	real to int32
#96	long	*fpi32tor32*	11		int32 to real32
#98	long	*fpi32tor64*	11		int32 to real64
#9A	long	*fpb32tor64*	10		bit32 to real64
#0D	seq	*fpunoround*	2		real64 to real32 w/o rounding

E   Instructions set reference

All transputer instructions are listed below ordered by their op-codes. The direct functions are listed first. The bottom 4 bits of any use of a direct function will be determined by the operand value of that function.

The operations are then listed giving the full sequence of bytes required to execute that operation.

E.1   Direct functions

Byte   Abbreviation

Byte	Abbrev	
#0x	*j*	jump
#1x	*ldlp*	load local pointer
#2x	*pfix*	prefix
#3x	*ldnl*	load non local
#4x	*ldc*	load constant
#5x	*ldnlp*	load non local pointer
#6x	*nfix*	negative prefix
#7x	*ldl*	load local
#8x	*adc*	add constant
#9x	*call*	call
#Ax	*cj*	conditional jump
#Bx	*ajw*	adjust workspace
#Cx	*eqc*	equals constant
#Dx	*stl*	store local
#Ex	*stnl*	store non local
#Fx	*opr*	operate

E.2   Operations

N.b. This is a list of all transputer operations. Some operations are only available on certain transputer variants.

Bytes	Abbreviation	
#F0	rev	reverse
#F1	lb	load byte
#F2	bsub	byte subscript
#F3	endp	end process
#F4	diff	difference
#F5	add	add
#F6	gcall	general call
#F7	in	input message
#F8	prod	product
#F9	gt	greater than
#FA	wsub	word subscript
#FB	out	output message
#FC	sub	subtract
#FD	startp	start process
#FE	outbyte	output byte
#FF	outword	output word
#21; #F0	seterr	set error
#21; #F2	resetch	reset channel
#21; #F3	csub0	check subscript from 0
#21; #F5	stopp	stop process
#21; #F6	ladd	long add
#21; #F7	stlb	store low priority back pointer
#21; #F8	sthf	store high priority front pointer
#21; #F9	norm	normalise
#21; #FA	ldiv	long divide
#21; #FB	ldpi	load pointer to instruction
#21; #FC	stlf	store low priority front pointer
#21; #FD	xdble	extend to double
#21; #FE	ldpri	load current priority
#21; #FF	rem	remainder
#22; #F0	ret	return
#22; #F1	lend	loop end
#22; #F2	ldtimer	load timer
#22; #F9	testerr	test error false and clear
#22; #FA	testpranal	test processor analysing
#22; #FB	tin	timer input
#22; #FC	div	divide
#22; #FE	dist	disable timer
#22; #FF	disc	disable channel
#23; #F0	diss	disable skip
#23; #F1	lmul	long multiply
#23; #F2	not	bitwise not
#23; #F3	xor	exclusive or
#23; #F4	bcnt	byte count
#23; #F5	lshr	long shift right
#23; #F6	lshl	long shift left
#23; #F7	lsum	long sum

Bytes   Abbreviation

Bytes	Abbreviation	
#23; #F8	*lsub*	long subtract
#23; #F9	*runp*	run process
#23; #FA	*xword*	extend to word
#23; #FB	*sb*	store byte
#23; #FC	*gajw*	general adjust workspace
#23; #FD	*savel*	save low priority queue registers
#23; #FE	*saveh*	save high priority queue registers
#23; #FF	*wcnt*	word count
#24; #F0	*shr*	shift right
#24; #F1	*shl*	shift left
#24; #F2	*mint*	mimimum integer
#24; #F3	*alt*	alt start
#24; #F4	*altwt*	alt wait
#24; #F5	*altend*	alt end
#24; #F6	*and*	and
#24; #F7	*enbt*	enable timer
#24; #F8	*enbc*	enable channel
#24; #F9	*enbs*	enable skip
#24; #FA	*move*	move message
#24; #FB	*or*	or
#24; #FC	*csngl*	check single
#24; #FD	*ccnt1*	check count from 1
#24; #FE	*talt*	timer alt start
#24; #FF	*ldiff*	long diff
#25; #F0	*sthb*	store high priority back pointer
#25; #F1	*taltwt*	timer alt wait
#25; #F2	*sum*	sum
#25; #F3	*mul*	multiply
#25; #F4	*sttimer*	store timer
#25; #F5	*stoperr*	stop on error
#25; #F6	*cword*	check word
#25; #F7	*clrhalterr*	clear halt-on-error
#25; #F8	*sethalterr*	set halt-on-error
#25; #F9	*testhalterr*	test halt-on-error
#25; #FA	*dup*	duplicate top of stack
#25; #FB	*move2dinit*	initialise data for 2 dimensional block move
#25; #FC	*move2dall*	2 dimensional block copy
#25; #FD	*move2dnonzero*	2 dimensional block copy non zero bytes
#25; #FE	*move2dzero*	2 dimensional block copy zero bytes
#26; #F3	*unpacksn*	unpack single length fp number
#26; #FC	*postnormsn*	post-normalise correction of single length fp number
#26; #FD	*roundsn*	round single length fp number
#27; #F1	*ldinf*	load single length infinity
#27; #F2	*fmul*	fractional multiply
#27; #F3	*cflerr*	check single length fp infinity or NaN
#27; #F4	*crcword*	calculate CRC on word
#27; #F5	*crcbyte*	calculate CRC on byte
#27; #F6	*bitcnt*	count bits set in word
#27; #F7	*bitrevword*	reverse bits in word
#27; #F8	*bitrevnbits*	reverse bottom n bits in word
#28; #F1	*wsubdb*	form double word subscript
#28; #F2	*fpldnldbi*	floating point load non local indexed double

Bytes		Abbreviation	
	#28; #F3	fpchkerr	check floating point error
	#28; #F4	fpstnldb	floating point store non local double
	#28; #F6	fpldnlsni	floating point load non local indexed single
	#28; #F7	fpadd	floating point add
	#28; #F8	fpstnlsn	floating point store non local single
	#28; #F9	fpsub	floating point subtract
	#28; #FA	fpldnldb	floating point load non local double
	#28; #FB	fpmul	floating point multiply
	#28; #FC	fpdiv	floating point divide
	#28; #FE	fpldnlsn	floating point load non local single
	#28; #FF	fpremfirst	floating point remainder first step
	#29; #F0	fpremstep	floating point remainder iteration step
	#29; #F1	fpnan	floating point nan
	#29; #F2	fpordered	floating point orderability
	#29; #F3	fpnotfinite	floating point finite
	#29; #F4	fpgt	floating point greater than
	#29; #F5	fpeq	floating point equality
	#29; #F6	fpi32tor32	int32 to real32
	#29; #F8	fpi32tor64	int32 to real64
	#29; #FA	fpb32tor64	bit32 to real64
	#29; #FC	fptesterr	test floating point error false and clear
	#29; #FD	fprtoi32	real to int32
	#29; #FE	fpstnli32	store non local int32
	#29; #FF	fpldzerosn	load zero single
	#2A; #F0	fpldzerodb	load zero double
	#2A; #F1	fpint	round to floating integer
	#2A; #F3	fpdup	floating point duplicate
	#2A; #F4	fprev	floating point reverse
	#2A; #F6	fpldnladddb	floating point load non local and add double
	#2A; #F8	fpldnlmuldb	floating point load non local and multiply double
	#2A; #FA	fpldnladdsn	floating point load non local and add single
	#2A; #FB	fpentry	floating point unit entry
	#2A; #FC	fpldnlmulsn	floating point load non local and multiply single
#41;	#2A; #FB	fpusqrtfirst	floating point square root first step
#42;	#2A; #FB	fpusqrtstep	floating point square root step
#43;	#2A; #FB	fpusqrtlast	floating point square root end
#44;	#2A; #FB	fpurp	set rounding mode to round positive
#45;	#2A; #FB	fpurm	set rounding mode to round minus
#46;	#2A; #FB	fpurz	set rounding mode to round zero
#47;	#2A; #FB	fpur32tor64	real32 to real64
#48;	#2A; #FB	fpur64tor32	real64 to real32
#49;	#2A; #FB	fpuexpdec32	divide by 2^{32}
#4A;	#2A; #FB	fpuexpinc32	multiply by 2^{32}
#4B;	#2A; #FB	fpuabs	floating point absolute
#4D;	#2A; #FB	fpunoround	real64 to real32 w/o rounding
#4E;	#2A; #FB	fpuchki32	check in range of type int 32
#4F;	#2A; #FB	fpuchki64	check in range of type int 64
#21; #41;	#2A; #FB	fpudivby2	divide by 2.0
#21; #42;	#2A; #FB	fpumulby2	multiply by 2.0
#22; #42;	#2A; #FB	fpurn	set rounding mode to round nearest
#22; #43;	#2A; #FB	fpuseterr	set floating point error
#29; #4C;	#2A; #FB	fpuclrerr	clear floating point error

F   Specification of instruction set

It is important when using transputer instructions to know the effect of those instructions on the state of the transputer. In particular it is important to know what happens to the information on the register stack. In the earlier sections of this guide an attempt has been made to explain what happens to these registers in cases where it is important — e.g. in some of the instructions used in the evaluation of expressions — but in other places these details have been omitted. The instruction descriptions that follow provide a more formal definition of them. The descriptions are intended to capture precisely what the effect of each instruction is. This is usually achieved by using mathematical relations that hold between the state of the transputer before and after the instruction has been executed. In some cases, to aid clarity and brevity, parts of the state changes are described textually.

The sections explaining how transputer instructions are used to implement high level language constructs should be sufficient to explain how each instruction is used. This section has been added to give a more precise definition of the effect of each instruction on the transputer state. It is realised that many readers will not be familiar with this style of specification. A brief explanation of some of the notation used is given so that it should be possible to understand most of the specification. The intention is that this section is only consulted to check if, for example, an instruction is defined to preserve the value in **Creg** rather than to find out what an instruction does.

F.1   Definitions

A few informal definitions are required to identify the wordlength of the transputer being specified. Note that the specifications of the instructions are the same for transputers of different wordlength apart from the values given to these constants.

wordlength and *bytesperword* are constants of the particular transputer being specified. *byteselectmask* and *byteselectlength* are derived from *wordlength* to enable the byte selector bits to be extracted from a pointer. *wordlength* and *bytesperword* are clearly linked by

$$wordlength = bytesperword \times 8$$

As was described earlier, *byteselectlength* is the smallest number of bits needed to distinguish the bytes in a word. *byteselectmask* is the mask used to extract these bits from a pointer. These can be deduced for any wordlength by solving the inequalities

$$2^{byteselectlength-1} < bytesperword \leq 2^{byteselectlength}$$
$$byteselectmask = 2^{byteselectlength} - 1$$

F.1.1   Data types

The basic data quantities are the **Word** and the **Byte**. A **Byte** is an unsigned integer b in the range $0 \leq b < 256$. A **Word** can be interpreted as an unsigned integer w in the range $0 \leq w < 2^{wordlength}$, or as a signed integer or as a bit pattern. As this is only an informal specification no further details on their definition will be given and the relevant interpretation of a **Word** at any point should be clear from its context. Where necessary operations are annotated with suffices to indicate whether the operation is being performed on the signed or unsigned interpretations.

F.1.2   The transputer state

The transputer state consists of the registers

> Areg, Breg, Creg, Oreg, Iptr, Wptr

the memory, which will be described later, and various flags and special registers such as the ErrorFlag, process queue pointers, clock registers, current priority level etc.

F.2   Reading a specification

The specification of each instruction is presented as a 'schema' of the following form.

abbreviation *code*	*name*
predicates defining effect of the instruction	
$\vdots$	

The value of registers etc. after the instruction will be specified in terms of their values before the instruction. The definitions will give a precise definition of the 'values' left in each register so that register allocation can be identified. Most of the predicates are of the form

> $register' = expression\ involving\ registers$

Primed names represent values after the instruction while unprimed names represent values before the instruction. For example, Areg represents the value of **Areg** before the execution of the instruction while Areg' represents the value of **Areg** afterwards. So the predicate above states that the register on the left hand side of the equality becomes equal to the value of the expression on the right hand side after the instruction has been executed. For example

> $Areg' = Breg + Areg$

states that after the instruction **Areg** will contain the sum of the values that were in **Breg** and **Areg** before the instruction. In addition

> $Oreg^o$

is used to hold the value of the operand register used in an instruction.

All of these predicates can be read together as a multiple assignment statement if necessary.

Quantities whose value after the instruction do not appear in the predicate part are **unchanged** by the instruction. An undefined value is represented by the symbol *undefined*.

The symbols *true* and *false* represent the machine representations of the booleans *TRUE* and *FALSE*. These are 1 and 0 respectively.

The symbol *NextInst* represents the address of the start of the next instruction in the code.

To simplify the definition of checked arithmetic the operators $+_{checked}$, $-_{checked}$ and $\times_{checked}$ will be used to denote the signed arithmetic operators that will side effect by setting the error flag in case of overflow.

In some places text is used to describe effects that cannot be described easily in the simplified specification language used here. As this is only an informal specification this is acceptable.

F.2.1   Timeslicing

If an instruction can cause timeslicing to occur then it must be assumed that all registers may be undefined after execution.

F.2.2   An example instruction specification — add

As an example take the add instruction. This is specified by

add	#05	add
Areg′ = Breg +checked Areg Breg′ = Creg Creg′ = *undefined* Iptr′ = NextInst ErrorFlag′ = *can be set by* +checked		

This states that

- Add has abbreviation *add* and operation code #05.

- The value of **Areg** after the operation is the sum of the values that were in **Areg** and **Breg** before the operation.

- The value that was in **Creg** has been popped into **Breg**.

- The value in **Creg** afterwards is not specified.

- **Iptr** is set to the start of the next instruction.

- The error flag will be set by an overflow in the sum of **Breg** and **Areg**

- The memory and the other flags are not affected by this operation as they are not mentioned in this specification.

F.2.3   Representing memory

The transputer's memory is used in three ways in the instruction set

- As **Byte** values stored at byte addresses — as in lb, sb, etc.

- As **Word** values stored at word addresses — as in ldnl, stnl, etc.

- As **Word** values stored at word offsets from **Wptr** — as in ldl, stl, etc.

These three representations will be called

    ByteMem
    Mem
    Workspace

respectively and always be assumed to be consistent with each other — i.e. changing an entry in Workspace will have the equivalent effect in ByteMem and Mem. The three representations should be seen as three methods of interpreting the same data.

As Mem is used to represent the **Word** values at word address, it is not appropriate to consider its value at addresses which are not word addresses. Therefore

> Mem *addr*

will be considered to be undefined if the byte selector of *addr* is not 0.

A transputer's memory consists of **Byte** values at **Word** addresses. However most accesses to memory deal in **Word** sized quantities. Also many instructions use **Word** offsets in addressing.

Index and ByteIndex will be used to form the address which is a given number of words or bytes past a base address respectively. They are defined to wrap the address space around when an overflow occurs. For example in the specification of ldnl the statement

> Areg$'$ = Mem (Index Areg Oreg$^\circ$)

is used. In this (Index Areg Oreg$^\circ$) is used to form the address that is Oreg$^\circ$ words from the address pointed to by Areg. These can be considered to be defined by

> Index x y = x + *bytesperword* $\times$ y
> ByteIndex x y = x + y

where the arithmetic 'wraps round' the address space — i.e. adding one to the address at the top of the address map produces the address of the bottom of the address map.

'Accessing' memory

The value of the word at address *addr* is simply

> Mem *addr*

Writing a word value *v* to memory at address *addr* is represented by

> Mem $\oplus$ { *addr* $\mapsto$ *v*}

This is because, in this style of specification, it is convenient to consider memory to be a function that when given an address evaluates to the contents of that address.

Reading a memory address is achieved by applying the memory function to that address.

Writing a value to memory is achieved by overwriting the memory function with a second function that contains the modified data. In the example above the memory Mem is overwritten (the $\oplus$ operator) by a function that maps ($\mapsto$) *addr* to *v*. This gives a function that is identical to Mem for all arguments apart from *addr* where it now evaluates to *v*. This represents a memory that used to be Mem but has now had *v* stored at location *addr*.

To demonstrate this modelling of memory consider the specification of store local

stl	#D_	store local
Areg$'$ = Breg		
Breg$'$ = Creg		
Creg$'$ = *undefined*		
Oreg$'$ = 0		
Iptr$'$ = *NextInst*		
Workspace$'$ = Workspace $\oplus$ { Oreg$^\circ$ $\mapsto$ Areg}		

This specifies that

- Store local has abbreviation stl and operation code #D_ — i.e. it is direct function #D.

- The evaluation stack has been popped up one place.

- **Oreg** is set to zero.

- **Iptr** is set to the start of the next instruction.

- The value that was in **Areg** has been stored into Workspace at the offset that was held in **Oreg**. This is equivalent to the address in Mem which is Oreg^o words from **Wptr** — i.e. at address Index Wptr Oreg^o.

- Mem' and ByteMem' will now differ from Mem and ByteMem as to take account of the modification made to Workspace.

F.2.4   Preconditions to instructions

Some instructions are only well defined under certain circumstances. These are specified by including extra predicates that define their preconditions. For example block move is only well defined when the two blocks do not overlap. The specification of block move is

move	#4A	move message
$\neg$ (Creg $\leq$ Breg < (Creg + Areg))		
$\neg$ (Breg $\leq$ Creg < (Breg + Areg))		
i.e. the two blocks do not overlap		
Areg' = *undefined*		
Breg' = *undefined*		
Creg' = *undefined*		
Iptr' = *NextInst*		
This copies Areg *bytes starting at address* Creg *to the block starting at address* Breg.		

The first two predicates are true only when the two blocks do not overlap. The specification is only well defined when all the predicates can be satisfied so this implies the the fact that the effect of a block move is undefined when the two blocks overlap.

F.3   Instruction specifications

F.3.1   Decoding an instruction

The lower four bits of the instruction are placed in the bottom of the operand register and the top four bits are interpreted as the function code.

$Oreg^o$ represents the value of the operand register after the decoding has taken place but before the selected instruction is executed.

Instruction_Decode
$Oreg^o = Oreg \lor ((Mem\ Iptr) \land \#F)$
$((Mem\ Iptr) \land \#F0) = pfix.code \Rightarrow pfix$
$((Mem\ Iptr) \land \#F0) = nfix.code \Rightarrow nfix$
$((Mem\ Iptr) \land \#F0) = opr.code \Rightarrow opr$
$((Mem\ Iptr) \land \#F0) = ldl.code \Rightarrow ldl$
$\vdots$
etc.

F.3.2   Prefixing and operate

pfix #2_	prefix
$Oreg' = Oreg^o \ll 4$	
$Iptr' = Iptr + 1$	

nfix #6_	negative prefix
$Oreg' = (BITNOT\ Oreg^o) \ll 4$	
$Iptr' = Iptr + 1$	

As these are not 'full' instructions in themselves but are used to build up an operand for a function the Iptr is explicitly incremented by 1 here.

opr #F_	operate
$Oreg' = 0$	
$Oreg^o = rev.code \Rightarrow rev$	
$Oreg^o = ret.code \Rightarrow ret$	
$\vdots$	
etc.	

F.3.3   Direct Functions

ldc #4_	load constant
$Areg' = Oreg^o$	
$Breg' = Areg$	
$Creg' = Breg$	
$Oreg' = 0$	
$Iptr' = NextInst$	

ldl	#7_	load local

Areg' = Workspace Oreg°
Breg' = Areg
Creg' = Breg
Oreg' = 0
Iptr' = _NextInst_

stl	#D_	store local

Areg' = Breg
Breg' = Creg
Creg' = _undefined_
Oreg' = 0
Iptr' = _NextInst_
Workspace' = Workspace ⊕ { Oreg° ↦ Areg}

ldlp	#1_	load local pointer

Areg' = Index Wptr Oreg°
Breg' = Areg
Creg' = Breg
Oreg' = 0
Iptr' = _NextInst_

adc	#8_	add constant

Areg' = Areg $+_{checked}$ Oreg°
Oreg' = 0
Iptr' = _NextInst_
ErrorFlag' _can be set by overflow from_ $+_{checked}$

eqc	#C_	equals constant

(Areg = Oreg°) ⇒ Areg' = _true_
(Areg ≠ Oreg°) ⇒ Areg' = _false_
Oreg' = 0
Iptr' = _NextInst_

_j_	#0_	jump

Oreg' = 0
Iptr' = ByteIndex _NextInst_ Oreg°
This instruction has the potential to cause a process to be timesliced

_cj_	#A_	conditional jump

Areg = 0 ⇒ Areg' = Areg
        Breg' = Breg
        Creg' = Creg
        Iptr' = ByteIndex _NextInst_ Oreg°
Areg ≠ 0 ⇒ Areg' = Breg
        Breg' = Creg
        Creg' = _undefined_
        Iptr' = _NextInst_
    Oreg' = 0

ldnl	#3_	load non-local

Areg ∧ *byteselectmask* = 0
Areg′ = Mem (Index Areg Oreg°)
Oreg′ = 0
Iptr′ = *NextInst*

stnl	#E_	store non-local

Areg ∧ *byteselectmask* = 0
Areg′ = Creg
Breg′ = *undefined*
Creg′ = *undefined*
Oreg′ = 0
Iptr′ = *NextInst*
Mem′ = Mem ⊕ { (Index Areg Oreg°) ↦ Breg}

ldnlp	#5_	load non-local pointer

Areg ∧ *byteselectmask* = 0
Areg′ = Index Areg Oreg°
Oreg′ = 0
Iptr′ = *NextInst*

call	#9_	call

Areg′ = *NextInst*
Oreg′ = 0
Wptr′ = Index Wptr (−4)
Iptr′ = ByteIndex *NextInst* Oreg°
Workspace′ = Shifted_Workspace ⊕ { 0 ↦ Iptr,
                                   1 ↦ Areg,
                                   2 ↦ Breg,
                                   3 ↦ Creg}
where Shifted_Workspace *is* Workspace *shifted up 4 words*
i.e. Workspace *addr* = Shifted_Workspace *addr+4*

ajw	#B_	adjust workspace

Oreg′ = 0
Wptr′ = Index Wptr Oreg°
Iptr′ = *NextInst*

F.3.4   Operations

The *opr* instruction selects the operation whose code is in Oreg. Each of these operations now needs to be specified. N.B. Oreg′ is set to 0 in the *opr* specification of which each of the following specifications is a component.

rev	#00	reverse

Areg′ = Breg
Breg′ = Areg
Iptr′ = *NextInst*

add	#05	add

Areg' = Breg +$_{checked}$ Areg
Breg' = Creg
Creg' = *undefined*
Iptr' = *NextInst*
ErrorFlag' = *can be set by* +$_{checked}$

sub	#0C	subtract

Areg' = Breg −$_{checked}$ Areg
Breg' = Creg
Creg' = *undefined*
Iptr' = *NextInst*
ErrorFlag' = *can be set by* −$_{checked}$

mul	#53	multiply

Areg' = Breg ×$_{checked}$ Areg
Breg' = Creg
Creg' = *undefined*
Iptr' = *NextInst*
ErrorFlag' = *can be set by* ×$_{checked}$

div	#2C	divide

$(Areg = 0) \vee (Areg = -1 \wedge Breg = -2^{wordlength-1}) \Rightarrow$ Areg' = *undefined*
$\qquad\qquad\qquad\qquad\qquad\qquad\qquad\qquad$ ErrorFlag' = set
$(Areg \neq 0) \wedge (Areg \neq -1 \vee Breg \neq -2^{wordlength-1}) \Rightarrow$ Areg' = Breg ÷ Areg
$\qquad\qquad\qquad\qquad\qquad\qquad\qquad\qquad$ ErrorFlag' = ErrorFlag

Breg' = Creg
Creg' = *undefined*
Iptr' = *NextInst*

rem	#1F	remainder

$(Areg = 0) \vee (Areg = -1 \wedge Breg = -2^{wordlength-1}) \Rightarrow$ Areg' = *undefined*
$\qquad\qquad\qquad\qquad\qquad\qquad\qquad\qquad$ ErrorFlag' = set
$(Areg \neq 0) \wedge (Areg \neq -1 \vee Breg \neq -2^{wordlength-1}) \Rightarrow$ Areg' = Breg *REM* Areg
$\qquad\qquad\qquad\qquad\qquad\qquad\qquad\qquad$ ErrorFlag' = ErrorFlag

Breg' = Creg
Creg' = *undefined*
Iptr' = *NextInst*

sum	#52	sum

Areg' = Breg +$_{unchecked}$ Areg
Breg' = Creg
Creg' = *undefined*
Iptr' = *NextInst*

diff	#04	difference

Areg' = Breg −$_{unchecked}$ Areg
Breg' = Creg
Creg' = *undefined*
Iptr' = *NextInst*

| *prod* | #08 | product |

Areg' = Breg $\times_{unchecked}$ Areg
Breg' = Creg
Creg' = *undefined*
Iptr' = *NextInst*

| *and* | #46 | and |

Areg' = Breg $\wedge$ Areg
Breg' = Creg
Creg' = *undefined*
Iptr' = *NextInst*

| *or* | #4B | or |

Areg' = Breg $\vee$ Areg
Breg' = Creg
Creg' = *undefined*
Iptr' = *NextInst*

| *xor* | #33 | exclusive or |

Areg' = Breg $><$ Areg
Breg' = Creg
Creg' = *undefined*
Iptr' = *NextInst*

| *not* | #32 | bitwise not |

Areg' = *BITNOT* Areg
Iptr' = *NextInst*

| *shl* | #41 | shift left |

Areg $<_{unsigned}$ *wordlength*
Areg' = Breg $\ll$ Areg
Breg' = Creg
Creg' = *undefined*
Iptr' = *NextInst*

| *shr* | #40 | shift right |

Areg $<_{unsigned}$ *wordlength*
Areg' = Breg $\gg$ Areg
Breg' = Creg
Creg' = *undefined*
Iptr' = *NextInst*

| *gt* | #09 | greater than |

Breg $>_{signed}$ Areg $\Rightarrow$ Areg' = *true*
Breg $\leq_{signed}$ Areg $\Rightarrow$ Areg' = *false*
Breg' = Creg
Creg' = *undefined*
Iptr' = *NextInst*

lend	#21	loop end

Creg' = *undefined*
count > 1 ⇒ Mem' = Mem ⊕ { (Index Breg 1) ↦ count − 1,
                                        Breg ↦ (Mem Breg) + 1}
             Iptr' = ByteIndex *NextInst* (−Areg)
count ≤ 1 ⇒ Mem' = Mem ⊕ { (Index Breg 1) ↦ count − 1}
             Iptr' = *NextInst*
where count = Mem (Index Breg 1)
This instruction has the potential to cause a process to be timesliced

bcnt	#34	byte count

Areg' = Areg × *bytesperword*
Iptr' = *NextInst*

wcnt	#3F	word count

Areg' = Areg ≫ ₐᵣᵢₜₕₘₑₜᵢ𝒸 *byteselectlength*
Breg' = Areg ∧ *byteselectmask*
Creg' = Breg
Iptr' = *NextInst*

ldpi	#1B	load pointer to instruction

Areg' = ByteIndex *NextInst* Areg
Iptr' = *NextInst*

mint	#42	minimum integer

Areg' = −$2^{wordlength-1}$
Breg' = Areg
Creg' = Breg
Iptr' = *NextInst*

bsub	#02	byte subscript

Areg' = ByteIndex Areg Breg
Breg' = Creg
Creg' = *undefined*
Iptr' = *NextInst*

wsub	#0A	word subscript

Areg' = Index Areg Breg
Breg' = Creg
Creg' = *undefined*
Iptr' = *NextInst*

move	#4A	move message

¬ (Creg ≤ Breg < (Creg + Areg))
¬ (Breg ≤ Creg < (Breg + Areg))
i.e. the two blocks do not overlap
Areg' = *undefined*
Breg' = *undefined*
Creg' = *undefined*
Iptr' = *NextInst*
This copies Areg *bytes starting at address* Creg *to the block starting at address* Breg. *This can be formally defined by the following predicate*
ByteMem' = ByteMem ⊕ (((ByteIndex Breg)⁻¹/{ 0 .. Areg−1});(ByteIndex Creg);ByteMem)

in	#07	input message

Areg' = *undefined*
Breg' = *undefined*
Creg' = *undefined*
Iptr' = *NextInst*
'input message of length Areg bytes from channel pointed to by Breg to memory at Creg'
This can cause the process to be descheduled

out	#0B	output message

Areg' = *undefined*
Breg' = *undefined*
Creg' = *undefined*
Iptr' = *NextInst*
'output message of length Areg bytes to channel pointed to by Breg from memory at Creg'
This can cause the process to be descheduled

lb	#01	load byte

Areg' = ByteMem Areg
Iptr' = *NextInst*

sb	#3B	store byte

Areg' = Creg
Breg' = *undefined*
Creg' = *undefined*
Iptr' = *NextInst*
ByteMem' = ByteMem ⊕ { Areg ↦ (Breg ∧ 255)}

outbyte	#0E	output byte

Areg' = *undefined*
Breg' = *undefined*
Creg' = *undefined*
Iptr' = *NextInst*
Workspace' = Workspace ⊕ { 0 ↦ *undefined* }
'output byte in Areg down channel pointed to by Breg'
This can cause the process to be descheduled

outword	#0F	output word

Areg' = *undefined*
Breg' = *undefined*
Creg' = *undefined*
Iptr' = *NextInst*
Workspace' = Workspace $\oplus$ { 0 $\mapsto$ *undefined* }
'output word in Areg down channel pointed to by Breg'
This can cause the process to be descheduled

gcall	#06	general call

Areg' = *NextInst*
Iptr' = Areg

gajw	#3C	general adjust workspace

Areg $\wedge$ *byteselectmask* = 0
Areg' = Wptr
Wptr' = Areg
Iptr' = *NextInst*

ret	#20	return

Wptr' = Index Wptr 4
Iptr' = Workspace 0   *n.b.*   Workspace *is wrt to* Wptr *and not* Wptr'
Mem' = Mem

startp	#0D	start process

'add process with workspace Areg and instruction pointer at offset of Breg bytes from Iptr' to current priority process queue'
Iptr' = *NextInst*

endp	#03	end process

Mem (Index Areg 1) = 1 $\Rightarrow$ 'continue as process with waiting workspace Areg'
Mem (Index Areg 1) $\neq$ 1 $\Rightarrow$ 'start next waiting process'
Mem' = Mem $\oplus$ { (Index Areg 1) $\mapsto$ (Mem (Index Areg 1)) $-$ 1)}

runp	#39	run process

'Add process with descriptor Areg to appropriate process queue'

stopp	#15	stop process

'stop current process leaving Iptr in workspace so it can be restarted and start next waiting process'

ldpri	#1E	load priority

Areg' = *current priority level*
Breg' = Areg
Creg' = Breg
Iptr' = *NextInst*

ldtimer	#22	load timer

Areg' = *value of current priority level clock*
Breg' = Areg
Creg' = Breg
Iptr' = *NextInst*

tin	#2B	timer input

Areg' = *undefined*
Breg' = *undefined*
Creg' = *undefined*
Iptr' = *NextInst*
'wait until time is AFTER Areg'
This can cause the process to be descheduled

The ALT instructions will be dealt with very informally. They have only limited meaning individually as they are specifically designed to be used in one way. All the alt, enb and dis instructions can affect locations Workspace 0 to Workspace −5 and these effects will not be described fully.

alt	#43	alt start

Iptr' = *NextInst*
'store flag to show enabling is occuring'

altwt	#44	alt wait

Areg' = *undefined*
Breg' = *undefined*
Creg' = *undefined*
Iptr' = *NextInst*
'set flag to show no branch has been selected yet and wait until one of the guards is ready'
This can cause the process to be descheduled

altend	#45	alt end

Iptr' = ByteIndex *NextInst* (Workspace 0)
'Set Iptr to first instruction of branch selected'

talt	#4E	timer alt start

Iptr' = *NextInst*
'store flag to show enabling is occuring and alt time not yet set'

taltwt	#51	timer alt wait

Areg' = *undefined*
Breg' = *undefined*
Creg' = *undefined*
Iptr' = *NextInst*
'set flag to show no branch has been selected yet, put alt time into the timer queue and wait until one of the guards is ready'
This can cause the process to be descheduled

enbs	#49	enable skip

Areg = *true* ⇒ 'set flag to show a guard is ready'
Areg' = Areg
Iptr' = *NextInst*

diss	#30	disable skip

Breg = *true* ∧ 'no branch selected'
   ⇒ 'select this branch'
      Areg′ = *true*
      Workspace′ = Workspace ⊕ { 0 ↦ Areg}
Breg ≠ *true* ∨ 'branch already selected'
   ⇒ Areg′ = *false*
      Workspace′ = Workspace
Breg′ = Creg
Creg′ = *undefined*
Iptr′ = NextInst

enbc	#48	enable channel

Areg = *true* ∧ 'no process waiting on channel Breg'
   ⇒ 'initiate communication on channel Breg'
Areg = *true* ∧ 'current process waiting on channel Breg'
   ⇒ 'already waiting on this channel so ignore'
Areg = *true* ∧ 'another process waiting on channel Breg'
   ⇒ 'set flag to show a guard is ready'
Areg′ = Areg
Breg′ = Creg
Creg′ = *undefined*
Iptr′ = NextInst

disc	#2F	disable channel

Breg = *true* ∧ 'channel Creg ready and no branch selected'
   ⇒ 'select this branch'
      Areg′ = *true*
      Workspace′ = Workspace ⊕ { 0 ↦ Areg}
Breg ≠ *true* ∨ 'channel Creg not ready or a branch already selected'
   ⇒ Areg′ = *false*
      Workspace′ = Workspace
Breg′ = *undefined*
Creg′ = *undefined*
Iptr′ = NextInst

enbt	#47	enable timer

Areg = *true* ∧ 'alt time not yet set'
   ⇒ 'Set time set flag and set alt time to time of guard'
Areg = *true* ∧ 'alt time set and earlier than this guard'
   ⇒ 'ignore this guard'
Areg = *true* ∧ 'alt time set and later than this guard'
   ⇒ 'set alt time to time of this guard'
Areg′ = Areg
Breg′ = Creg
Creg′ = *undefined*
Iptr′ = NextInst

dist	#2E	disable timer

Breg = *true* ∧ 'time later than guard's time and no branch selected'
    ⇒ 'select this branch'
        Areg′ = *true*
        Workspace′ = Workspace ⊕ { 0 ↦ Areg}
Breg ≠ *true* ∨ 'time earlier than guards time or branch already selected'
    ⇒ Areg′ = *false*
        Workspace′ = Workspace
Breg′ = *undefined*
Creg′ = *undefined*
Iptr′ = *NextInst*

csub0	#13	check subscript from 0

Areg′ = Breg
Breg′ = Creg
Creg′ = *undefined*
Breg ≥ $_{unsigned}$ Areg ⇒ ErrorFlag′ = set
Breg < $_{unsigned}$ Areg ⇒ ErrorFlag′ = ErrorFlag
Iptr′ = *NextInst*

ccnt1	#4D	check count from 1

Areg′ = Breg
Breg′ = Creg
Creg′ = *undefined*
Breg = 0 ⇒ ErrorFlag′ = set
Breg > $_{unsigned}$ Areg ⇒ ErrorFlag′ = set
0 < $_{unsigned}$ Breg ≤ $_{unsigned}$ Areg ⇒ ErrorFlag′ = ErrorFlag
Iptr′ = *NextInst*

testerr	#29	test error false and clear

ErrorFlag = set ⇒ Areg′ = *false*
ErrorFlag = clear ⇒ Areg′ = *true*
Breg′ = Areg
Creg′ = Breg
ErrorFlag′ = clear
Iptr′ = *NextInst*

stoperr	#55	stop on error

ErrorFlag = set ⇒ 'schedule next waiting process'
ErrorFlag = clear ⇒ Iptr′ = *NextInst*

seterr	#10	set error

ErrorFlag′ = set
Iptr′ = *NextInst*

xword	#3A	extend to word

0 ≤ Breg < Areg ⇒ Areg′ = Breg
−Areg ≤ Breg < 0 ⇒ Areg′ = Breg − (2 × Areg)
Breg′ = Creg
Creg′ = *undefined*
Iptr′ = *NextInst*

cword	#56	check word

$(\text{Breg} \geq \text{Areg}) \vee (\text{Breg} < -\text{Areg}) \Rightarrow \text{ErrorFlag}' = \text{set}$
$(\text{Breg} < \text{Areg}) \vee (\text{Breg} \geq -\text{Areg}) \Rightarrow \text{ErrorFlag}' = \text{ErrorFlag}$
$\text{Areg}' = \text{Breg}$
$\text{Breg}' = \text{Creg}$
$\text{Creg}' = undefined$
$\text{Iptr}' = NextInst$

xdble	#1D	extend to double

$\text{Areg} < 0 \Rightarrow \text{Breg}' = -1$
$\text{Areg} \geq 0 \Rightarrow \text{Breg}' = 0$
$\text{Creg}' = \text{Breg}$
$\text{Iptr}' = NextInst$

csngl	#4C	check single

$(\text{Areg} < 0 \wedge \text{Breg} \neq -1) \vee (\text{Areg} \geq 0 \wedge \text{Breg} \neq 0) \Rightarrow \text{ErrorFlag}' = \text{set}$
$\neg((\text{Areg} < 0 \wedge \text{Breg} \neq -1) \vee (\text{Areg} \geq 0 \wedge \text{Breg} \neq 0)) \Rightarrow \text{ErrorFlag}' = \text{ErrorFlag}$
$\text{Breg}' = \text{Creg}$
$\text{Creg}' = undefined$
$\text{Iptr}' = NextInst$

ladd	#16	long add

$\text{Areg}' = (\text{Breg} +_{\text{checked}} \text{Areg}) +_{\text{checked}} (\text{Creg} \wedge 1)$
$\text{Breg}' = undefined$
$\text{Creg}' = undefined$
$\text{Iptr}' = NextInst$
$\text{ErrorFlag}'$ set if $(\text{Breg} + \text{Areg}) + (\text{Creg} \wedge 1)$ overflows

lsub	#38	long subtract

$\text{Areg}' = (\text{Breg} -_{\text{checked}} \text{Areg}) -_{\text{checked}} (\text{Creg} \wedge 1)$
$\text{Breg}' = undefined$
$\text{Creg}' = undefined$
$\text{Iptr}' = NextInst$
$\text{ErrorFlag}'$ set if $(\text{Breg} - \text{Areg}) - (\text{Creg} \wedge 1)$ overflows

lsum	#37	long sum

$\text{Areg}' = (\text{Breg} + \text{Areg}) + (\text{Creg} \wedge 1)$
$\text{Breg}' = carry\ from\ (\text{Breg} + \text{Areg}) + (\text{Creg} \wedge 1)$
$\text{Creg}' = undefined$
$\text{Iptr}' = NextInst$

ldiff	#4F	long difference

$\text{Areg}' = (\text{Breg} - \text{Areg}) - (\text{Creg} \wedge 1)$
$\text{Breg}' = borrow\ from\ (\text{Breg} - \text{Areg}) - (\text{Creg} \wedge 1)$
$\text{Creg}' = undefined$
$\text{Iptr}' = NextInst$

lmul	#31	long multiply

$\text{Areg}' = low\ word\ of\ (\text{Breg} \times \text{Areg}) + \text{Creg}$
$\text{Breg}' = high\ word\ of\ (\text{Breg} \times \text{Areg}) + \text{Creg}$
$\text{Creg}' = undefined$
$\text{Iptr}' = NextInst$

ldiv	#1A	long divide

$\text{Creg} \geq \text{Areg} \Rightarrow \text{ErrorFlag}' = \text{set}$
$\text{Creg} < \text{Areg} \Rightarrow \text{ErrorFlag}' = \text{ErrorFlag}$
$\qquad\qquad \text{Areg}' = (\text{Creg} \times 2^{\text{wordlength}} + \text{Breg}) \div \text{Areg}$
$\qquad\qquad \text{Breg}' = (\text{Creg} \times 2^{\text{wordlength}} + \text{Breg}) \; REM \; \text{Areg}$
$\qquad\qquad \text{Creg}' = undefined$
$\text{Iptr}' = \text{NextInst}$

lshl	#36	long shift left

$0 \leq \text{Areg} \leq 2 \times \text{wordlength}$
$(\text{Breg}' \times 2^{\text{wordlength}} + \text{Areg}') = ((\text{Creg} \times 2^{\text{wordlength}} + \text{Breg}) \times 2^{\text{Areg}}) \; REM \; 2^{2 \times \text{wordlength}}$
$\text{Creg}' = undefined$
$\text{Iptr}' = \text{NextInst}$

lshr	#35	long shift right

$0 \leq \text{Areg} \leq 2 \times \text{wordlength}$
$(\text{Breg}' \times 2^{\text{wordlength}} + \text{Areg}') = (\text{Creg} \times 2^{\text{wordlength}} + \text{Breg}) \; DIV \; 2^{\text{Areg}}$
$\text{Creg}' = undefined$
$\text{Iptr}' = \text{NextInst}$

norm	#19	normalise

$(\text{Breg}' \times 2^{\text{wordlength}} + \text{Areg}') = (\text{Breg} \times 2^{\text{wordlength}} + \text{Areg}) \times 2^{\text{Creg}'}$
$((\text{Breg} = 0 \land \text{Areg} = 0 \land \text{Creg}' = 2 \times \text{wordlength})$
$\qquad\qquad\qquad\qquad \lor$
$(\text{Breg}' \geq_{\text{unsigned}} 2^{\text{wordlength}-1}))$
$\text{Iptr}' = \text{NextInst}$

resetch	#12	reset channel

$\text{Areg}' = \text{Mem Areg}$
$\text{Iptr}' = \text{NextInst}$
$\text{Mem}' = \text{Mem} \oplus \{ \text{Areg} \mapsto NotProcess.p\}$
if Areg pointed to link channel then the link hardware is reset

testpranal	#2A	test processor analysing

$\text{Areg}' = $ *true if processor analysed rather than reset last, false otherwise*
$\text{Breg}' = \text{Areg}$
$\text{Creg}' = \text{Breg}$
$\text{Iptr}' = \text{NextInst}$

sthf	#18	store high priority front pointer

$\text{Areg}' = \text{Breg}$
$\text{Breg}' = \text{Creg}$
$\text{Creg}' = undefined$
$\text{Iptr}' = \text{NextInst}$
$\text{FPtrReg}_0 = \text{Areg}$

stlf	#1C	store low priority front pointer

$\text{Areg}' = \text{Breg}$
$\text{Breg}' = \text{Creg}$
$\text{Creg}' = undefined$
$\text{Iptr}' = \text{NextInst}$
$\text{FPtrReg}_1 = \text{Areg}$

sttimer #54	store timer
Areg′ = Breg Breg′ = Creg Creg′ = *undefined* Iptr′ = *NextInst* ClockReg$_0$ = Areg ClockReg$_1$ = Areg 'and start the clocks'	

sthb #50	store high priority back pointer
Areg′ = Breg Breg′ = Creg Creg′ = *undefined* Iptr′ = *NextInst* BPtrReg$_0$ = Areg	

stlb #17	store low priority back pointer
Areg′ = Breg Breg′ = Creg Creg′ = *undefined* Iptr′ = *NextInst* BPtrReg$_1$ = Areg	

saveh #3E	save high priority queue registers
Areg′ = Breg Breg′ = Creg Creg′ = *undefined* Iptr′ = *NextInst* Mem′ = Mem $\oplus$ { (Index Areg 0) $\mapsto$ FPtrReg$_0$, (Index Areg 1) $\mapsto$ BPtrReg$_0$}	

savel #3D	save low priority queue registers
Areg′ = Breg Breg′ = Creg Creg′ = *undefined* Iptr′ = *NextInst* Mem′ = Mem $\oplus$ { (Index Areg 0) $\mapsto$ FPtrReg$_1$, (Index Areg 1) $\mapsto$ BPtrReg$_1$}	

clrhalterr #57	clear halt-on-error
HaltOnErrorFlag′ = clear Iptr′ = *NextInst*	

sethalterr #58	set halt-on-error
HaltOnErrorFlag′ = set Iptr′ = *NextInst*	

testhalterr	#59	test halt-on-error

HaltOnErrorFlag = set $\Rightarrow$ Areg' = *true*
HaltOnErrorFlag = clear $\Rightarrow$ Areg' = *false*
Breg' = Areg
Creg' = Breg
Iptr' = *NextInst*

F.3.5   Fractional multiply — IMS T414 and IMS T800 only

fmul	#72	fractional multiply

Areg' = $2^{-(\text{wordlength}-1)} \times$ (Breg $\times$ Areg)
Breg' = Creg
Creg' = *undefined*
ErrorFlag' *is set by* $(-1) \times_{\text{fractional}} (-1)$
Iptr' = *NextInst*

F.3.6   Floating point handling — IMS T414 only

unpacksn	#63	unpack single length fp number

Areg' = *fraction field contents of Areg*
Breg' = *exponent field contents of Areg*
Creg' = 4 $\times$ Breg + *type of Areg*
where the type is 0 for Areg zero, 1 for Areg denormalised or normalised, 2 for Areg an infinity and
3 for Areg a Not-a-Number
Iptr' = *NextInst*

roundsn	#6D	round single length fp number

Areg' = *rounded and packed floating point number where initially*
            Creg *was exponent*
            Breg *was fraction*
            Areg *was guard word*
Breg' = *undefined*
Creg' = *undefined*
Iptr' = *NextInst*

postnormsn	#6C	post-normalise correction of single length fp number

perform postnormalise correction on floating point number where
            normalised fraction is in Breg *(high word) and* Areg *(guard word)*
            normalising shift length is in Creg
            and exponent is in Workspace 0
Areg' = *postnormalised guard word*
Breg' = *postnormalised fraction word*
Creg' = *postnormalised exponent*
Iptr' = *NextInst*

ldinf	#71	load single length fp infinity

Areg' = *single length floating point +infinity*
Breg' = Areg
Creg' = Breg
Iptr' = *NextInst*

cflerr #73	check single length fp infinity or NaN

Areg $\in$ Inf $\cup$ NaN $\Rightarrow$ ErrorFlag' = set
Areg $\notin$ Inf $\cup$ NaN $\Rightarrow$ ErrorFlag' = ErrorFlag
Iptr' = *NextInst*

F.4   Additional non floating point instructions on IMS T800

dup #5A	duplicate top of stack

Areg' = Areg
Breg' = Areg
Creg' = Breg
Iptr' = *NextInst*

move2dinit #5B	initialise data for 2 dimensional block move

Areg' = *undefined*
Breg' = *undefined*
Creg' = *undefined*
Iptr' = *NextInst*
set up first 3 parameters for 2d block move
Areg *contains the length of block,* Breg *the destination stride and* Creg *the source stride*

move2dall #5C	2 dimensional block copy

precondition: the two blocks do not overlap
Areg *contains the width of block,* Breg *the destination address and* Creg *the source address*
Areg' = *undefined*
Breg' = *undefined*
Creg' = *undefined*
Iptr' = *NextInst*
Mem' = Mem $\oplus$ *source block translated to destination*

move2dnonzero #5D	2 dimensional block copy non zero bytes

precondition: the two blocks do not overlap
Areg *contains the width of block,* Breg *the destination address and* Creg *the source address*
Areg' = *undefined*
Breg' = *undefined*
Creg' = *undefined*
Iptr' = *NextInst*
Mem' = Mem $\oplus$ *non zero bytes of source block translated to destination*

move2dzero #5E	2 dimensional block copy zero bytes

precondition: the two blocks do not overlap
Areg *contains the width of block,* Breg *the destination address and* Creg *the source address*
Areg' = *undefined*
Breg' = *undefined*
Creg' = *undefined*
Iptr' = *NextInst*
Mem' = Mem $\oplus$ *zero bytes of source block translated to destination*

crcword	#74	calculate CRC on word

Areg' = *CRC of* Areg *with generator* Creg *and accumulated CRC* Breg
Breg' = Creg
Creg' = *undefined*
Iptr' = *NextInst*

crcbyte	#75	calculate CRC on byte

Areg' = *CRC of top byte of* Areg *with generator* Creg *and accumulated CRC* Breg
Breg' = Creg
Creg' = *undefined*
Iptr' = *NextInst*

bitcnt	#76	count bits set in word

Areg' = Breg + *number of bits set in Areg*
Breg' = Creg
Creg' = *undefined*
Iptr' = *NextInst*

bitrevword	#77	reverse bits in word

Areg' = *reversed bit pattern of* Areg
Iptr' = *NextInst*

bitrevnbits	#78	reverse bottom n bits of word

Areg' = *bottom* Areg *bits of* Breg *reversed*
Breg' = Creg
Creg' = *undefined*
Iptr' = *NextInst*

wsubdb	#81	form double word subscript

Areg' = Index Areg (Breg × 2)
Breg' = Creg
Creg' = *undefined*
Iptr' = *NextInst*

G   Specification of floating point unit instructions

The operations that make use of the floating point unit on the IMS T800 will be specified in a similar manner to the rest of the instruction set. Again this is done fairly informally although as in the specification of the main transputer instructions some initial definitions are treated more rigorously.

G.1   Datatypes

The basic datatypes used are the occam types **INT32**, **INT64**, **REAL32**, **REAL64** and **BOOL**. The internal representation in the floating point unit of real numbers, the floating_point_register, stores both the value of the number it contains as well as the length of the format of that number.

Type conversions between the basic types is performed in the specifications in the occam style — i.e. if X is 2.3 (REAL32) then (**INT32 TRUNC** X) will be 2 (INT32). If a rounding mode such as **TRUNC** is not given then the mode in Round_Mode will be used. Use of **INT**∞ for type conversion converts to a member of **Z** — the set of all integers. When retyping is needed — interpreting the same bit pattern as a different type — the the keyword **RETYPE** will be used. For example the following predicate holds

$$1.0 \ (\textbf{REAL64}) = (\textbf{RETYPE REAL64} \ [\#00000000, \#3FF00000])$$

since the representation of 1.0 (**REAL64**) is #3FF0000000000000. The explicit retyping is sometimes omitted if it can be easily deduced from the types required in the context.

Conversions between **REAL**s and internal representations in floating_point_registers are performed by the following functions

unpack.sn : **REAL32** → floating_point_register
unpack.db : **REAL64** → floating_point_register
pack.sn : floating_point_register → **REAL32**
pack.db : floating_point_register → **REAL64**
$\forall$ r:**REAL32** . (*unpack.sn* r).length = SN
$\forall$ r:**REAL64** . (*unpack.db* r).length = DB
dom *pack.sn* = { f:floating_point_register | f.length = SN}
dom *pack.db* = { f:floating_point_register | f.length = DB}

The function *fv* maps a floating_point_register into the real number that it represents — it is undefined on Not-a-Numbers and infinities.

fv : floating_point_register → **R**

In some cases the value of a register may be well specified but difficult to express clearly at the informal level of this document. Often this value will be a partially computed result from a component of an instruction sequence performing a larger operation — such as remainder. '$\bowtie$' is used in these cases. If appropriate a description of what that register contains will be added in text at the bottom of the specification.

Inf and NaN are the sets of all floating_point_registers that represent infinities or Not-a-Numbers respectively.

The specification of each floating point unit operation is done in a similar style to that for the basic transputer instruction set. Because of the concurrent nature of the floating point unit the results may not have been calculated when the main processor finishes executing the instruction but the synchronisation between the two units ensures that the results will be established before they can be observed.

All floating point unit instructions set Iptr′ to *NextInst* so this is ommitted for brevity.

G.2   Floating point unit state

The state of the floating point unit consists of the registers

FAreg, FBreg, FCreg

the floating point error flag and rounding mode

FP_ErrorFlag, Round_Mode

This state is added to the main transputer state.

Almost all the specifications of the main transputer instructions still hold as the floating point unit and the main processor are totally independent when not executing floating point unit instructions. The only exceptions are those instructions which can cause descheduling. In these cases the floating point registers must be assumed to be undefined after the instruction as the process may have been descheduled.

G.3   Floating point unit entry

The special *fpentry* instruction is used to access certain of the operations. Its specification is

fpentry #AB	floating point unit entry
Areg′ = Breg Breg′ = Creg Creg′ = *undefined* 'execute operation Areg on floating point unit'	

Instructions that are accessed via an *fpentry* will have

value

as their code value in the following specifications where *value* is the value to be loaded into **Areg** prior to executing *fpentry*.

G.4   Floating point unit operations

fpdup #A3	floating duplicate
FAreg′ = FAreg FBreg′ = FAreg FCreg′ = FBreg Round_Mode′ = ToNearest	

fprev	#A4	floating reverse

FAreg' = FBreg
FBreg' = FAreg
FCreg' = FCreg

Round_Mode' = ToNearest

fpldnlsn	#8E	floating load non local single

Areg ∧ *byteselectmask* = 0

Areg' = Breg
Breg' = Creg
Creg' = *undefined*

FAreg' = *unpack.sn* (**RETYPE REAL32** Mem Areg)
FBreg' = FAreg
FCreg' = FBreg

Round_Mode' = ToNearest

fpldnldb	#8A	floating load non local double

Areg ∧ *byteselectmask* = 0

Areg' = Breg
Breg' = Creg
Creg' = *undefined*

FAreg' = *unpack.db* (**RETYPE REAL64** [Mem Areg, Mem (Index Areg 1)])
FBreg' = FAreg
FCreg' = FBreg

Round_Mode' = ToNearest

fpldnlsni	#86	floating load non local indexed single

Areg ∧ *byteselectmask* = 0

Areg' = Creg
Breg' = *undefined*
Creg' = *undefined*

FAreg' = *unpack.sn* (**RETYPE REAL32** Mem (Index Areg Breg))
FBreg' = FAreg
FCreg' = FBreg

Round_Mode' = ToNearest

fpldnldbi	#82	floating load non local indexed double

Areg $\land$ *byteselectmask* = 0

Areg' = Breg
Breg' = Creg
Creg' = *undefined*

FAreg' = *unpack.db* (**RETYPE REAL64** [Mem (Index Areg Breg),
                                    Mem (Index (Index Areg Breg) 1)])
FBreg' = FAreg
FCreg' = FBreg

Round_Mode' = ToNearest

fpstnlsn	#88	floating store non local single

Areg $\land$ *byteselectmask* = 0
FAreg.length = SN

Areg' = Breg
Breg' = Creg
Creg' = *undefined*

FAreg' = FBreg
FBreg' = FCreg
FCreg' = *undefined*

Mem' = Mem $\oplus$ { Areg $\mapsto$ **RETYPE INT32** *pack.sn* (FAreg)}
Round_Mode' = ToNearest

fpstnldb	#84	floating store non local double

Areg $\land$ *byteselectmask* = 0
FAreg.length = DB

Areg' = Breg
Breg' = Creg
Creg' = *undefined*

FAreg' = FBreg
FBreg' = FCreg
FCreg' = *undefined*

Mem' = Mem $\oplus$ { Areg $\mapsto$ lo, (Index Areg 1) $\mapsto$ hi}
        where [lo, hi] = **RETYPE [ ] INT32** *pack.db* (FAreg)
Round_Mode' = ToNearest

fpurn	@#22	set rounding mode to round to nearest

Round_Mode' = ToNearest

fpurz	@#06	set rounding mode to round to zero

Round_Mode' = ToZero

fpurp	@#04	set rounding mode to round to plus infinity

Round_Mode' = ToPlusInfinity

fpurm	@#05	set rounding mode to round to minus infinity

Round_Mode' = ToMinusInfinity

fpadd	#87	floating point add

FAreg.length = FBreg.length

FAreg' = FBreg +$_{\text{IEEE}}$ FAreg
FBreg' = FCreg
FCreg' = *undefined*

FP_Error_Flag' = *can be set by error from* (FBreg +$_{\text{IEEE}}$ FAreg)
Round_Mode' = ToNearest

fpsub	#89	floating point subtract

FAreg.length = FBreg.length

FAreg' = FBreg −$_{\text{IEEE}}$ FAreg
FBreg' = FCreg
FCreg' = *undefined*

FP_Error_Flag' = *can be set by error from* (FBreg −$_{\text{IEEE}}$ FAreg)
Round_Mode' = ToNearest

fpmul	#8B	floating point multiply

FAreg.length = FBreg.length

FAreg' = FBreg ×$_{\text{IEEE}}$ FAreg
FBreg' = FCreg
FCreg' = *undefined*

FP_Error_Flag' = *can be set by error from* (FBreg ×$_{\text{IEEE}}$ FAreg)
Round_Mode' = ToNearest

fpdiv	#8C	floating point divide

FAreg.length = FBreg.length

FAreg' = FBreg ÷$_{\text{IEEE}}$ FAreg
FBreg' = FCreg
FCreg' = *undefined*

FP_Error_Flag' = *can be set by error from* (FBreg ÷$_{\text{IEEE}}$ FAreg)
Round_Mode' = ToNearest

fpusqrtfirst	@#01	floating point square root first step

FAreg' = ⋈
FBreg' = ⋈
FCreg' = ⋈

FP_Error_Flag' = ⋈
Round_Mode' = ToNearest

The values in the registers are well defined but, as they contain a partial result, no attempt to describe their contents will be made here

fpusqrtstep @#02	floating point square root step

FAreg$'$ = ⋈
FBreg$'$ = ⋈
FCreg$'$ = ⋈

Round_Mode$'$ = ToNearest

fpusqrtlast @#03	floating point square root last step

FAreg$'$ = ⋈
FBreg$'$ = *undefined*
FCreg$'$ = *undefined*

Round_Mode$'$ = ToNearest

	square root instruction sequence

FAreg$'$ = SQRT$_{\text{IEEE}}$ (FAreg)
FBreg$'$ = *undefined*
FCreg$'$ = *undefined*

FP_Error_Flag$'$ = *can be set by error from* SQRT$_{\text{IEEE}}$ FAreg
Round_Mode$'$ = ToNearest

fpremfirst #8F	floating point remainder first step

FAreg.length = FBreg.length

Areg$'$ = ⋈
Breg$'$ = Areg
Creg$'$ = Breg

FAreg$'$ = ⋈
FBreg$'$ = ⋈
FCreg$'$ = ⋈

FP_Error_Flag$'$ = ⋈
Round_Mode$'$ = ToNearest

fpremstep #90	floating point remainder iteration step

FAreg.length = FBreg.length

Areg$'$ = ⋈
Breg$'$ = Areg
Creg$'$ = Breg

FAreg$'$ = ⋈
FBreg$'$ = ⋈
FCreg$'$ = ⋈

Round_Mode$'$ = ToNearest

	remainder instruction sequence
FAreg.length = FBreg.length Areg' = *undefined* Breg' = *undefined* Creg' = *undefined* FAreg' = FBreg REM$_{\text{IEEE}}$ FAreg FBreg' = ⋈ FCreg' = *undefined* FP_Error_Flag' = *can be set by error from* (FBreg REM$_{\text{IEEE}}$ FAreg) Round_Mode' = ToNearest *The value of FBreg' will be the quotient used to produce the remainder when (FBreg.exp - FAreg.exp) is ≤ 20 for single length and ≤ 30 for double length operands. This is intended to correct the rounding error in argument reduction and is explained in greater detail in the arithmetic operations section earlier.*	

fpldzerosn #9F	floating load zero single
FAreg' = *unpack.sn* (0.0 **REAL32**) FBreg' = FAreg FCreg' = FBreg Round_Mode' = ToNearest	

fpldzerodb #A0	floating load zero double
FAreg' = *unpack.db* (0.0 **REAL64**) FBreg' = FAreg FCreg' = FBreg Round_Mode' = ToNearest	

fpumulby2 @#12	floating multiply by 2
FAreg' = FAreg ×$_{\text{IEEE}}$ 2 FP_Error_Flag' *can be set by error from* FAreg ×$_{\text{IEEE}}$ 2 Round_Mode' = ToNearest	

fpudivby2 @#11	floating divide by 2
FAreg' = FAreg ÷$_{\text{IEEE}}$ 2 FP_Error_Flag' *can be set by error from* FAreg ÷$_{\text{IEEE}}$ 2 Round_Mode' = ToNearest	

fpuexpinc32 @#0A	floating multiply by 2^{32}
FAreg' = FAreg ×$_{\text{IEEE}}$ 2^{32} FP_Error_Flag' *can be set by error from* FAreg ×$_{\text{IEEE}}$ 2^{32} Round_Mode' = ToNearest	

fpuexpdec32	@#09	floating divide by 2^{32}

FAreg$'$ = FAreg $\div_{\text{IEEE}}$ 2^{32}

FP_Error_Flag$'$ *can be set by error from* FAreg $\div_{\text{IEEE}}$ 2^{32}
Round_Mode$'$ = ToNearest

fpuabs	@#0B	floating point absolute value

FAreg$'$ = |FAreg|

FP_Error_Flag$'$ = FP_Error_Flag $\vee$ (FAreg $\in$ NaN $\cup$ Inf)
Round_Mode$'$ = ToNearest

fpldnladdsn	#AA	floating load non local and add single

Areg $\wedge$ *byteselectmask* = 0
FAreg.len = SN

Areg$'$ = Breg
Breg$'$ = Creg
Creg$'$ = *undefined*

FAreg$'$ = FAreg $+_{\text{IEEE}}$ *unpack.sn* (**RETYPE REAL32** Mem Areg)
FBreg$'$ = FBreg
FCreg$'$ = *undefined*

FP_Error_Flag = *can be set by error from* $+_{\text{IEEE}}$
Round_Mode$'$ = ToNearest

fpldnladddb	#A6	floating load non local and add double

Areg $\wedge$ *byteselectmask* = 0
FAreg.len = DB

Areg$'$ = Breg
Breg$'$ = Creg
Creg$'$ = *undefined*

FAreg$'$ = FAreg $+_{\text{IEEE}}$ *unpack.db* (**RETYPE REAL64** [Mem Areg, Mem (Index Areg 1)])
FBreg$'$ = FBreg
FCreg$'$ = *undefined*

FP_Error_Flag = *can be set by error from* $+_{\text{IEEE}}$
Round_Mode$'$ = ToNearest

---

fpldnlmulsn	#AC	floating load non local and multiply single

Areg ∧ *byteselectmask* = 0
FAreg.len = SN

Areg′ = Breg
Breg′ = Creg
Creg′ = *undefined*

FAreg′ = FAreg ×$_{IEEE}$ *unpack.sn* (**RETYPE REAL32** Mem Areg)
FBreg′ = FBreg
FCreg′ = *undefined*

FP_Error_Flag = *can be set by error from* ×$_{IEEE}$
Round_Mode′ = ToNearest

---

fpldnlmuldb	#A8	floating load non local and multiply double

Areg ∧ *byteselectmask* = 0
FAreg.len = DB

Areg′ = Breg
Breg′ = Creg
Creg′ = *undefined*

FAreg′ = FAreg ×$_{IEEE}$ *unpack.db* (**RETYPE REAL64** [Mem Areg, Mem (Index Areg 1)])
FBreg′ = FBreg
FCreg′ = *undefined*

FP_Error_Flag = *can be set by error from* ×$_{IEEE}$
Round_Mode′ = ToNearest

---

fpchkerr	#83	check floating error

Error_Flag′ = Error_Flag ∨ FP_Error_Flag
Round_Mode′ = ToNearest

---

fptesterr	#9C	test floating error false and clear

FP_Error_Flag = clear ⇒ Areg′ = *true*
FP_Error_Flag ≠ clear ⇒ Areg′ = *false*
Breg′ = Areg
Creg′ = Breg

Round_Mode′ = ToNearest
FP_Error_Flag′ = clear

---

fpuseterr	@#23	set floating error

FP_Error_Flag′ = set
Round_Mode′ = ToNearest

---

fpuclrerr	@#9C	clear floating error

FP_Error_Flag′ = clear
Round_Mode′ = ToNearest

fpgt	#94	floating point greater than

FAreg.length = FBreg.length

Areg′ = FBreg > FAreg
Breg′ = Areg
Creg′ = Breg

FAreg′ = FCreg
FBreg′ = *undefined*
FCreg′ = *undefined*

FP_Error_Flag′ = FP_Error_Flag ∨ (FAreg ∈ Inf ∪ NaN) ∨ (FBreg ∈ Inf ∪ NaN)
Round_Mode′ = ToNearest

fpeq	#95	floating point equals

FAreg.length = FBreg.length

Areg′ = FBreg = FAreg
Breg′ = Areg
Creg′ = Breg

FAreg′ = FCreg
FBreg′ = *undefined*
FCreg′ = *undefined*

FP_Error_Flag′ = FP_Error_Flag ∨ (FAreg ∈ Inf ∪ NaN) ∨ (FBreg ∈ Inf ∪ NaN)
Round_Mode′ = ToNearest

fpordered	#92	floating point orderability

Areg′ = (FAreg ∉ NaN) ∧ (FBreg ∉ NaN)
Breg′ = Areg
Creg′ = Breg

Round_Mode′ = ToNearest

fpnan	#91	floating point test for NaN

Areg′ = FAreg ∈ NaN
Breg′ = Areg
Creg′ = Breg

Round_Mode′ = ToNearest

fpnotfinite	#93	floating point test for not finite

Areg′ = FAreg ∈ (Inf ∪ NaN)
Breg′ = Areg
Creg′ = Breg

Round_Mode′ = ToNearest

---

fpur32tor64	@#07	real32 to real64

FAreg.length = SN

FAreg' = *unpack.db* (**REAL64** *pack.sn* (FAreg))

FP_Error_Flag' = FP_Error_Flag $\lor$ (FAreg $\in$ Inf $\cup$ NaN)
Round_Mode' = ToNearest

---

fpur64tor32	@#08	real64 to real32

FAreg.length = DB

FAreg' = *unpack.sn* (**REAL32** *pack.db* (FAreg))
        with behaviour on NaNs as described earlier

FP_Error_Flag' = FP_Error_Flag $\lor$ overflow $\lor$ (FAreg $\in$ Inf $\cup$ NaN)
Round_Mode' = ToNearest

---

fpint	#A1	round to floating integer

FAreg' = **REAL** (**INT**∞ *pack* FAreg)

Round_Mode' = ToNearest

This rounds FAreg, wrt Round_Mode, to a floating point number of the same format with an integer value.

---

fpstnli32	#9E	store non local int32

fv FAreg $\in$ [MinINT32,MaxINT32]

Areg' = Breg
Breg' = Creg
Creg' = *undefined*

FAreg' = FBreg
FBreg' = FCreg
FCreg' = *undefined*

Mem' = Mem $\oplus$ { Areg $\mapsto$ **INT32 TRUNC** *pack* (FAreg)}
Round_Mode' = ToNearest

where pack is either *pack.sn* or *pack.db* depending on FAreg.len.

---

fpuchki32	@#0E	check in int32 range

FAreg *'has an integer value'*

FP_Error_Flag' = FP_Error_Flag $\lor$ (*fv* FAreg $\notin$ [MinINT32,MaxINT32])
Round_Mode' = ToNearest

---

fpuchki64	@#0F	check in int64 range

FAreg *'has an integer value'*

FP_Error_Flag' = FP_Error_Flag $\lor$ (*fv* FAreg $\notin$ [MinINT64,MaxINT64])
Round_Mode' = ToNearest

fprtoi32	#9D	real to int32

FAreg.len = SN

FAreg$'$ = **REAL** (**INT**∞ *pack* FAreg)

FP_Error_Flag$'$ = FP_Error_Flag $\vee$ (**INT32** *pack.sn* (FAreg) $\notin$ [MinINT32,MaxINT32])
Round_Mode$'$ = ToNearest
*This rounds FAreg, wrt Round_Mode, to a floating point number of the same format with an integer value and sets error if this lies outside the **INT32** range*

fpi32tor32	#96	load int32 as real32

Areg$'$ = Breg
Breg$'$ = Creg
Creg$'$ = *undefined*

FAreg$'$ = *unpack.sn* (**REAL32** Mem Areg)
FBreg$'$ = FAreg
FCreg$'$ = FBreg

Round_Mode$'$ = ToNearest

fpi32tor64	#98	load int32 as real64

Areg$'$ = Breg
Breg$'$ = Creg
Creg$'$ = *undefined*

FAreg$'$ = *unpack.db* (**REAL64** Mem Areg)
FBreg$'$ = FAreg
FCreg$'$ = FBreg

Round_Mode$'$ = ToNearest

fpb32tor64	#9A	load unsigned word as real64

Areg$'$ = Breg
Breg$'$ = Creg
Creg$'$ = *undefined*

FAreg$'$ = $\bowtie$
FBreg$'$ = FAreg
FCreg$'$ = FBreg

Round_Mode$'$ = ToNearest

fpunoround	@#0D	real64 to real32 without rounding

FAreg.length = DB

FAreg$'$ = $\bowtie$

Round_Mode$'$ = ToNearest

changes exponent bias and length of FAreg *to DB*

---

real to INT32 code sequence

Areg' = Breg
Breg' = Creg
Creg' = *undefined*

FAreg' = FBreg
FBreg' = FCreg
FCreg' = *undefined*

FP_Error_Flag' = FP_Error_Flag ∨ (**INT**∞ *pack* (FAreg) ∉ [MinINT32,MaxINT32])
Mem' = Mem ⊕ { Areg ↦ **RETYPE INT32** *pack* (FAreg)}
Round_Mode' = ToNearest

---

real to INT64 code sequence

Areg' = Breg
Breg' = Creg
Creg' = *undefined*

FAreg' = FBreg
FBreg' = FCreg
FCreg' = *undefined*

FP_Error_Flag' = FP_Error_Flag ∨ (**INT**∞ *pack* (FAreg) ∉ [MinINT64,MaxINT64])
Mem' = Mem ⊕ { Areg ↦ lo, (Index Areg 1) ↦ hi}
        where [lo, hi] = **RETYPE [ ] INT32** (**INT64** *pack* FAreg)
Round_Mode' = ToNearest

INT64 to REAL32 code sequence

Areg' = Breg
Breg' = Creg
Creg' = *undefined*

FAreg' = *unpack.db* (**REAL32** value)
        where value = **RETYPE INT64** [Mem Areg, Mem (Index Areg 1)]
FBreg' = FAreg
FCreg' = FBreg

Round_Mode' = ToNearest

INT64 to REAL64 code sequence

Areg' = Breg
Breg' = Creg
Creg' = *undefined*

FAreg' = *unpack.db* (**REAL64** value)
        where value = **RETYPE INT64** [Mem Areg, Mem (Index Areg 1)])
FBreg' = FAreg
FCreg' = FBreg

Round_Mode' = ToNearest

Instruction index

Index